HEALTH FRAMEWORK

for California Public Schools
Kindergarten Through Grade Twelve

Publishing Information

When the *Health Framework for California Public Schools* was adopted by the California State Board of Education on December 11, 1992, the members of the State Board were the following: Joseph H. Stein, President; Gerti B. Thomas, Vice-President; Irene Cheng, Kathryn Dronenburg, Yvonne W. Larsen, Dorothy J. Lee, Frank R. Light, S. William Malkasian, Marion McDowell, and Benjamin F. Montoya.

This publication was prepared for printing by staff members of the Bureau of Publications: editing, Edward O'Malley; design, Steve Yee; layout, Steve Yee and Juan Sanchez; typesetting, Donna Kurtz.

The framework was published by the Department of Education, 721 Capitol Mall, Sacramento, California (mailing address: P.O. Box 944272, Sacramento, CA 94244-2720). It was printed by the Office of State Printing and distributed under the provisions of the Library Distribution Act and *Government Code* Section 11096.

ISBN 0-8011-1064-5

Ordering Information

Copies of this publication are available for $8.50 each, plus sales tax for California residents, from the Bureau of Publications, Sales Unit, California Department of Education, P.O. Box 271, Sacramento, CA 95812-0271; FAX (916) 323-0823. See page 232 for complete information on payment, including credit card purchases.

A list of other publications available from the Department appears on pages 231–32. A free illustrated *Publications Catalog* and supplement describing available Department publications may be obtained by writing to the address given above or by calling the Sales Unit at (916) 445-1260.

Contents

Preface

The State Board of Education and the California Department of Education are pleased to present the *Health Framework for California Public Schools, Kindergarten Through Grade Twelve.* This document urges educators, parents, and community members to come together to support the health of young people. For too many years health education has been caught up in arguments over whether supporting the health of students is the job of the school or of parents. Clearly, both are responsible. Arguments of this kind serve only to detract from collaborative efforts to find solutions. While this debate goes on, research has documented that our children and youths are making poor health choices that are undermining the quality of their lives today and will continue to do so well into the future. Other indicators of health problems being experienced by our children are a decline in levels of fitness; common use of alcohol, tobacco, and other drugs; increased numbers of teenage pregnancies; and continued dangerous behavior exposing young people to fatal or debilitating injuries, sexually transmitted diseases, or chronic physical problems later in life.

The time has come to end the debate and begin to act. This framework, which serves as a blueprint for action, states the position that as a society we are all responsible for supporting the health of young people. Although schools alone cannot solve the health problems of children and youths, they are essential partners in the required collaborative effort. The intent of this framework is not to usurp parental authority but to bring together schools, parents, and the community to help young people develop lifelong healthy behaviors.

This framework calls for students to be engaged in learning about health and for schools to develop a system for supporting the health of students. Although health education should begin in the home and preschool well before kindergarten, this

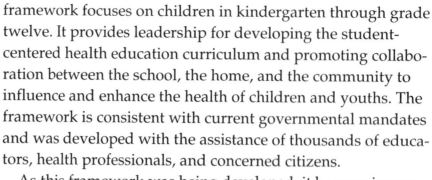

framework focuses on children in kindergarten through grade twelve. It provides leadership for developing the student-centered health education curriculum and promoting collaboration between the school, the home, and the community to influence and enhance the health of children and youths. The framework is consistent with current governmental mandates and was developed with the assistance of thousands of educators, health professionals, and concerned citizens.

As this framework was being developed, it became increasingly obvious that many individuals and organizations willing to support the healthy development of children and youths often became confused in their collaborative efforts because of inconsistency in definitions related to health education. To prevent such confusion, the State Board of Education and the Department of Education decided to offer the following definitions, which have been adapted from a report of the Association for the Advancement of Health Education:[1]

Health: A state of complete physical, mental, and social well-being, not merely the absence of disease and infirmity.

Health literacy: The capacity of an individual to obtain, interpret, and understand basic health information and services and the competence to use such information and services in ways that are health-enhancing.

Comprehensive school health system: An organized set of policies, procedures, and activities developed and implemented through a collaborative effort that includes parents, the school, and the community. The system is designed to protect and promote the health and well-being of students and staff. A comprehensive school health system includes health education, physical education, health services, nutrition services, psychological and

[1] "Report of the 1990 Joint Committee on Health Education Terminology," *Journal of Health Education*, Vol. 22, No. 2 (March-April, 1991), 104.

counseling services, a safe and healthy school environment, health promotion for staff, and parent and community involvement.

Health education: One component of a comprehensive school health system. It includes the development, delivery, and evaluation of a planned, sequential curriculum for students in kindergarten through grade twelve and for parents and school staff and is designed to influence positively the knowledge, attitudes, skills, and behaviors of individuals related to health. Health education addresses the four unifying ideas of health literacy and the following content areas: personal health; consumer and community health; injury prevention and safety; alcohol, tobacco, and other drugs; nutrition; environmental health; family living; individual growth and development; and communicable and chronic diseases.

Other documents have used the terms *comprehensive health education, comprehensive school health education, school health education,* or *comprehensive school health instruction* to describe health education that addresses the nine content areas listed previously. To avoid confusion with the term *comprehensive school health system,* this document uses the term *health education.* However, that choice should not be seen as an attempt to undermine the purpose of addressing all nine content areas and all four unifying ideas.

You are all invited to use this framework to support and enhance the health of children and youths. We are convinced that the ultimate responsibility for implementing this framework does not rest solely with classroom teachers. Although classroom teachers do play a critical role in implementation as they model good health practices and involve students in health education in meaningful ways, we all have an important role in supporting and enhancing the health of our young people. As an African folk saying acknowledges, "It takes an

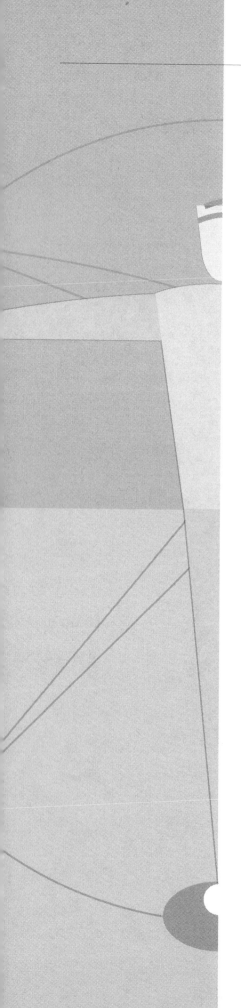

entire community to raise a child." The time has come for all of us to work together to ensure that our young people have the good health they need for a bright future.

WILLIAM D. DAWSON
Acting State Superintendent
of Public Instruction

HARVEY HUNT
Deputy Superintendent
Curriculum and Instructional
Leadership Branch

JOSEPH H. STEIN
President
California State Board
of Education

FRED TEMPES
Associate Superintendent
and Director
Curriculum, Instruction, and
Assessment Division

JANE HENDERSON
Assistant Superintendent
and Director
Interagency Children and
Youth Services Division

Acknowledgments

The development of this framework represents an unusually broad-scale effort. Many educators contributed to the document's original development; many others gave generously of their time in making revisions and additions to the framework, which was approved by the State Board of Education.

Overall guidance for the development of the framework was provided by the Chair, Health Subject Matter Committee, Curriculum Development and Supplemental Materials Commission (Curriculum Commission):

Eugene Flores, Arroyo Grande High School, Lucia Mar Unified School District

The Health Curriculum Framework and Criteria Committee, which consisted of nine California health educators and health professionals, was chaired by:

Justin Cunningham, Healthy Kids Regional Center, Region IX, San Diego County Office of Education

The other committee members were:

Claudia Baker, Los Angeles Unified School District

Dianne Changnon, Somerset Senior Elementary School, Sylvan Union Elementary School District

Linda Davis-Alldritt, Elk Grove Unified School District

Ellen Jones, Alameda County Office of Education

Shirley Knight-Lopez, Pajaro Valley Unified School District

Nathan Matza, Westminister High School, Huntington Beach Union High School District

Note: The locations of all persons listed in the Acknowledgements were current when this document was being prepared.

Cornelia Owens, Los Angeles Unified School District

Marilynn Wells, Alhambra City Elementary and High School District

The principal writer of the field-review version of this document was **William Boly**.

Chapter 3 of this document is based on preliminary work done by a committee of educators during 1989-90. The committee had begun to draft a model curriculum guide in health. Unfortunately, because of budget cuts the model curriculum guide was not completed. Members of the model curriculum guide committee were:

Peter Cortese, California State University, Long Beach

Justin Cunningham, San Diego County Office of Education

Gus Dalis, Los Angeles County Office of Education

Margaret Leeds, Beverly Hills High School, Beverly Hills Unified School District

Ric Loya, California Association of School Health Educators

Pamela Luna, Riverside County Office of Education

Priscilla Naworski, Comprehensive Health Education Resource Center, Alameda County Office of Education

Staff support from the California Department of Education to the model curriculum guide committee was provided by:

Amanda Dew Manning, **Jennifer Ekstedt**, and **Jacqui Smith**, Healthy Kids, Healthy California Office

The following individuals provided detailed information for Chapter 3 of the framework:

Ruth Bowman, Washington Unified School District

Justin Cunningham, San Diego County Office of Education

Joan Davies, Alameda County Office of Education

Pamela Luna, Riverside County Office of Education

Priscilla Naworski, Comprehensive Health Education Resource Center, Alameda County Office of Education

Jean Varden, Ventura County Office of Education

Overall coordination for the development, field review, and preparation of the framework was provided by:

Glen Thomas, Curriculum Frameworks and Instructional Resources Office, California Department of Education

The final stages of the development of the framework were directed by:

Justin Cunningham, San Diego County Office of Education

Ellen Jones, Alameda County Office of Education

with critical support from:

Nancy Sullivan, Curriculum Frameworks and Instructional Resources Office, California Department of Education

The State Board of Education's liaisons to the Curriculum Commission, **Kathryn Dronenburg** and **Sark "Bill" Malkasian**, provided invaluable direction and support in the final stages of development.

The principal writer of the final version of this document was **Hank Resnik**.

Staff support from the California Department of Education was provided throughout by:

Jennifer Ekstedt, Healthy Kids, Healthy California Office

Ples Griffin, Health Promotion Office

Robert Ryan, Healthy Kids, Healthy California Office

Nancy Sullivan, Curriculum Frameworks and Instructional Resources Office

In addition, many other individuals in the California Department of Education provided assistance during the development process, most notably:

Janice DeBenedetti, Home Economics Education Unit

Mary Lu Graham, Migrant Education Program

Emily Nahat, Interagency Youth and Children Services

Dennis Parker, Categorical Programs Division

Roberta Peck, Nutrition and Food Service Education Section

Jacqui Smith, Healthy Kids, Healthy California Office

Janine Swanson, Special Education Division

Kathy Yeates, Healthy Kids, Healthy California Office

Members of the Health Subject Matter Committee of the Curriculum Commission responsible for overseeing the development of the framework, including the field review, were:

Del Alberti, Washington Unified School District

Gloria Blanchette, Sacramento Unified School District

Dan Chernow, Pacific Theaters Corporation, Los Angeles

Bruce Fisher, Fortuna Elementary School, Fortuna Union Elementary School District

Eugene Flores (Chair, 1992), Arroyo Grande High School, Lucia Mar Unified School District

Harriett Harris, Del Mar Elementary School, Fresno Unified School District

Charles Kloes, Beverly Hills High School, Beverly Hills Unified School District

Charles Koepke (deceased), Upland Junior High School, Upland Unified School District

Tom Vasta (Chair, 1991), Elk Grove Unified School District

Vivian Lee Ward, Sequoia High School, Sequoia Union High School District

Chapter 1

The Vision: Health Literacy, Healthy Schools, Healthy People

"We need to make a national commitment to health education that is far greater than the routine and merely ceremonial attention we usually give it. . . . We need to teach youngsters that they must take charge of their health—all of their lives. . . . And we must do more than teach; we must set an example in the way we live."[1]

[1] C. Everett Koop, M.D., *Koop: The Memoirs of America's Family Doctor*. New York: Random House, 1991, p. 290.

In recent decades Americans have successfully coped with serious health problems. Many diseases and illnesses, such as polio and diphtheria, that once threatened vast numbers of people can now be prevented or treated effectively. As a result, a growing percentage of the population is staying healthier and living longer. However, far too many children and youths die because of injuries that are unintentional or result from violent behavior, and others compromise their health through unhealthy behaviors, such as using alcohol, tobacco, or other drugs. In addition, diseases brought on by unhealthy behaviors often cause the premature deaths of adults. Responding to these health problems requires a commitment to health education. Individuals must understand the role they must play in protecting, maintaining, and promoting their health and the health of others through healthy behaviors and choices.

Two factors central to this new approach to health education are as follows:

E mphasis must be placed on developing lifelong, positive health-related attitudes and behaviors.

- Emphasis must be placed on developing lifelong, positive health-related attitudes and behaviors. Such attitudes and behaviors begin to be developed in the home. But the school, working in close partnership with families and communities, is also an appropriate arena for development and reinforcement.[2]

- Health education in the schools must be supported by a comprehensive schoolwide system to promote children's health and must be developed and sustained by the collaborative efforts of school personnel, parents, school board members, community leaders, and health and social services agencies and providers.

---

[2] In this document the term *community* includes religious institutions, community leaders, businesses, health-care providers, and other agencies and organizations involved in children's development.

When these elements are in place, children and youths can be helped to develop a lifelong commitment to their own health and well-being.

Throughout this framework the knowledge, skills, and behaviors needed for healthy living are referred to as health literacy. According to the Association for the Advancement of Health Education, health literacy is "the capacity of an individual to obtain, interpret, and understand basic health information and services and the competence to use such information and services in ways which are health-enhancing."[3] A health-literate person understands scientifically based principles of health promotion and disease prevention, incorporates that knowledge into personal health-related attitudes and behaviors, and makes good health a personal priority.

This framework is based on the premise that health literacy is as important in today's complex, challenging world as linguistic, mathematical, and scientific literacy. The major goal of this framework is to describe health education and schoolwide health promotion strategies that will help children and youths become health-literate individuals with a lifelong commitment to healthy living.

Today, students are being asked to become involved in their schooling. They are expected to explore concepts in depth, analyze and solve realistic problems, and work cooperatively on tasks that develop and enhance their conceptual understanding. Health education focused on developing health literacy through a student-centered curriculum will enhance school-reform efforts and the understanding students have of health. Specifically, because its every aspect is tangibly connected to life and students' experiences, effective health education provides abundant opportunities for engaging students in purpose-

*H*ealth literacy is the capacity of an individual to obtain, interpret, and understand basic health information and services and the competence to use such information and services in ways which are health-enhancing.

—Journal of Health Education

---

[3]"Report of the 1990 Joint Committee on Health Education Terminology," *Journal of Health Education*, Vol. 22, No. 2 (1991), 104.

ful learning. Health-literate students will make a commitment to their own health and the health of others, enhancing school efforts to involve students in collaborative, meaningful learning experiences.

Unifying Ideas of Health Literacy

Health education focused on developing health literacy through a student-centered curriculum will enhance school-reform efforts and the understanding students have of health.

Health-literate individuals develop a growing mastery of knowledge, skills, and behaviors in four key areas critical to healthy living:

- *Acceptance of personal responsibility for lifelong health.* Health-literate individuals acknowledge that they have some control over their health, incorporate health-related knowledge into everyday behavior, and make a lifelong commitment to healthy living.

- *Respect for and promotion of the health of others.* Health-literate individuals understand and acknowledge the effects of personal behavior on the health and well-being of others. In addition, they understand the influence that people have on the environment and the way in which elements within the environment affect the health of groups and individuals. They translate this understanding into concern for the health of others in the family, school, peer group, and community.

- *An understanding of the process of growth and development.* Health-literate individuals understand and acknowledge the aspects of physical, mental, emotional, and social growth and development common to all people as well as those aspects that are unique to individuals. They respect the dignity of

4

all individuals and recognize that people continue to develop throughout their lives.

- *Informed use of health-related information, products, and services.* Health-literate individuals select and use available health-related information, products, and services carefully and wisely. Being health literate involves the ability to think critically about health-related information and be a selective consumer of health-related services and products.

The four unifying ideas of health literacy are central themes throughout this framework and are reiterated and reinforced in a variety of contexts.

The School's Role in Promoting Children's Health

Growing numbers of children are coming to school with a variety of health-related problems that make successful learning difficult or impossible, and many children in school routinely participate in behaviors that endanger their health. Many of the most serious health problems in our society affect the school-age population. A Children's Defense Fund report concluded that because of declining access to health services, children under eighteen years of age are at increasing risk of contracting infectious diseases and developing physical and mental disabilities. The report also pointed to the rising incidence of such preventable childhood diseases as measles, mumps, and rubella.[4] A national study on adolescents conducted by the

[4] *The Health of America's Children, 1992.* Washington, D.C.: Children's Defense Fund, 1992, pp. 1–32.

U.S. Centers for Disease Control and Prevention (CDC) found alarming levels of the use of alcohol and other drugs, weapon-carrying among high school students, early sexual activity, and suicide. CDC has determined that the most detrimental health-risk behaviors practiced by young people fall into six categories: (1) behaviors that result in unintentional or intentional injuries; (2) use of alcohol and other drugs; (3) sexual behaviors that result in HIV infection, other sexually transmitted diseases, or unintended pregnancy; (4) use of tobacco; (5) unhealthy diet; and (6) reduced physical activity.[5]

Trends in California are consistent with disturbing national findings. The state leads the nation in the birth rate for unmarried teens and the percentage of incarcerated juveniles, many of whom are confined, directly or indirectly, because of their use of alcohol or other drugs or because of their possession or use of weapons. Further, California's children tend to be physically unfit. They have higher percentages of body fat, are less physically active, and score lower on objective measures of physical fitness than in the past. Injuries, intentional or unintentional, which are the leading cause of death and disability among children and youths in California, have had an enormous impact. On average eight children in California die from injuries every day, and many more are seriously disabled.

Educators and policymakers at all levels have acknowledged the seriousness of children's health problems and the implications for education. *Healthy People 2000*, a U.S. government document that articulates a national framework for health policy, calls for a commitment to three broad goals to help the nation fulfill its potential: (1) an increase in the span of healthy life for Americans; (2) a reduction in health dispari-

---

[5] *Chronic Disease and Health Promotion: Reprints from the MMWR 1990-1991 Youth Risk Behavior Surveillance System.* Atlanta: U.S. Centers for Disease Control and Prevention, n.d.

For the first time in recent history, the next generation of Californians may not be as well off as the one which preceded it.

—Children Now
1992 Annual Report:
Saving the Dream

ties among Americans; and (3) access to preventive services for all Americans.[6] (See "Selected Healthy People 2000 Objectives Related to Schools," pages 8–9.) An article appearing in *Public Health Reports* emphasizes the combined roles of the education and health sectors in promoting lifelong good health.[7] The Healthy Kids, Healthy California Initiative, launched by the California Department of Education in 1989, and the Healthy Start Initiative (Senate Bill 620/1991) support the development of a positive, health-oriented school climate that recognizes health as being intimately linked to learning.

An emphasis on health is consistent with the goals for school reform in California. The major policy and planning documents that will influence California's schools for many years to come acknowledge that good health is basic to academic success.[8] A common theme is the need for schools to take an active role in developing and promoting the physical, mental, emotional, and social health of students. The documents also call for students to be engaged in meaningful work. Because health is relevant to students, health-related tasks can be used to capture student interest and enhance development of knowledge and skills in other curriculum areas.

Working with families and the community, schools have a unique opportunity to influence the health of children positively. In the past many schools resisted allocating resources to health beyond the bare minimum because evidence of its benefits was insufficient. Health seemed to have little relevance to day-to-day learning. Today, however, the benefits of health education and comprehensive school health ap-

---

[6] *Healthy People 2000: National Health Promotion and Disease Prevention Objectives.* Washington, D.C.: U.S. Department of Health and Human Services, Public Health Service, 1991, p. 6.

[7] A.C. Novello and others, "Healthy Children Ready to Learn: An Essential Collaboration Between Health and Education," *Public Health Reports*, Vol. 107, No. 1 (1992), 3–14.

[8] *Here They Come: Ready or Not; It's Elementary; Caught in the Middle; Second to None.* Published by the California Department of Education. Ordering information can be found at the back of this publication.

Selected *Healthy People 2000* Objectives Related to Schools

■ Increase to at least 75 percent the proportion of the nation's elementary and secondary schools that provide planned and sequential kindergarten through twelfth grade quality school health education. (Objective 8.4)

■ Increase to at least 50 percent the proportion of children and adolescents in first through twelfth grade who participate in daily school physical education. (Objective 1.8)

■ Increase to at least 90 percent the proportion of school lunch and breakfast services and child care food services with menus that are consistent with the nutrition principles in the *Dietary Guidelines for Americans*. (Objective 2.17)

■ Increase to at least 75 percent the proportion of the nation's schools that provide nutrition education from preschool through twelfth grade, preferably as part of quality school health education. (Objective 2.19)

From *Healthy People 2000: National Health Promotion and Disease Prevention Objectives.*

8

■ Establish tobacco-free environments and include tobacco use prevention in the curricula of all elementary, middle, and secondary schools, preferably as part of quality school health education. (Objective 3.10)

■ Provide to children in all school districts and private and secondary school educational programs on alcohol and other drugs, preferably as a part of quality school health education. (Objective 4.13)

■ Increase to at least 50 percent the proportion of elementary and secondary schools that teach nonviolent conflict resolution skills, preferably as part of quality school health education. (Objective 7.16)

■ Provide academic instruction on injury prevention and control, preferably as part of quality school health education, in at least 50 percent of public school systems (kindergarten through grade twelve). (Objective 9.18)

■ Increase to at least 95 percent the proportion of schools that have age-appropriate HIV education curricula for students in fourth through twelfth grade, preferably as part of quality school health education. (Objective 18.10)

■ Include instruction in sexually transmitted disease transmission prevention in the curricula of all middle and secondary schools, preferably as part of quality school health education. (Objective 19.12) proaches are clear. Many studies have found that school-based programs have brought about positive changes in a wide range of health-related behaviors among children, such as decision making and the ability to resist negative influences.[9] Researchers have found that instruction combining scientifically based information about health issues and continual reinforcement of positive health behaviors can also be effective.

Through education and comprehensive prevention strategies developed and implemented with parent involvement and education, schools can influence health behaviors significantly. They can state explicitly that certain behaviors are unhealthy but that other behaviors will enhance health and well-being. For example, schools can state that (1) violent behavior and actions that demean others are not acceptable; (2) alcohol, tobacco, and other drugs are not healthy and should not be used by children and youths; (3) sexual activity is not appropriate for young people; (4) safety practices should be followed and protective equipment and devices, such as seat belts and helmets, should be used; and (5) excessive consumption of fat and insufficient physical activity are not healthy but healthy food choices and physical activity can enhance health. Schools can teach and model healthy choices and empower young people to take responsibility for their own health and well-being.

Given the needs of today's children and the potential of schools to address children's health issues, schools must make health a priority in the curriculum and the overall school program. Because basic patterns of healthy living are formed in childhood and adolescence, schools, working in partnership with families and communities, are an ideal place to promote healthy attitudes and behaviors.

Working with families, . . . schools can influence health behaviors significantly. They can state explicitly that certain behaviors are unhealthy but that other behaviors will enhance health. Schools can teach and model healthy choices.

---

[9] D. Kirby and others, "Reducing the Risk: Impact of a New Curriculum on Sexual Risk-taking," *Journal of School Health*, Vol. 23, No. 6 (1991), 253–63. See also J.R. Seffrin, "The Comprehensive School Health Curriculum: Closing the Gap Between State-of-the-Art and State-of-the-Practice," *Journal of School Health*, Vol. 60, No. 4 (1990), 151–56.

Collaboration to Benefit the Whole Child

The health of children and their success in school are intimately linked.[10] Increasingly, the value and importance of educating the whole child, including focusing on children's health, is being supported by empirical studies. Inadequate nutrition and a wide range of negative and self-destructive behaviors, such as the use of alcohol, tobacco, and other drugs, have been linked to poor school performance. The converse is also true; that is, children who are helped to accept responsibility for their health are more likely to succeed in school and to become healthier, more responsible, and more successful adults. Schools are collaborating with parents and the community to address problems and behaviors that influence school performance. That approach is central to *Not Schools Alone*, which charts the course for alcohol, tobacco, and other drug education and prevention programs in California schools.[11]

Not Schools Alone emphasizes the importance of the school and the community in influencing children's health. Children and adolescents are more likely to practice healthy behaviors when those behaviors are broadly supported at school, at home, and in the community. A variety of *risk factors* influence whether or not a child will be healthy and will maintain a commitment to health. The school, the home, the community, and the peer group are four major areas of a child's life in which these risk factors may be found. The risk factors include, among others, economic deprivation, neighborhood disintegration, poor family-management practices, peers who use alcohol and other drugs, low expectations for children's success, and

> **S**chool programs need to recognize the bidirectional connection between health and education. Children must be healthy in order to be educated and children must be educated in order to stay healthy.
>
> —*Public Health Reports*

---

[10] *School Health: Helping Children Learn.* Alexandria, Va.: National School Boards Association, 1991, pp. 1–5. See also *Promoting Health Education in Schools: A Critical Issues Report.* Arlington, Va.: American Association of School Administrators, 1985, pp. 7–9.

[11] *Not Schools Alone.* Sacramento: California Department of Education. 1991. Ordering information can be found at the back of this publication.

The resilient child . . . is effective in work, play, and relationships. Possesses healthy expectancies and a positive outlook. Possesses self-esteem and internal locus of control. Maintains self-discipline. Has developed problem-solving and critical-thinking skills. Uses humor.

academic failure. Although some risk factors are far beyond a school's control, others can be addressed directly and effectively through health education supported by collaborative efforts that include parents, the school, and the community.

Balancing, buffering, and reducing risk in children's lives are *protective factors*. They include having opportunities to practice health-related skills, such as decision-making or refusal skills; knowing that clearly defined expectations and norms exist for appropriate behavior at school and at home; experiencing positive bonding to the family, the school, peers, and the community; and receiving recognition for participation in positive activities and personal accomplishments. These protective factors lead to the development of a sense of personal competence and resiliency. Together, schools, families, and the community can work to strengthen the protective factors and build resiliency. The physical, emotional, and social benefits of such collaborative efforts can be significant.

The Benefits of Prevention

Promoting children's health can be highly cost-effective for schools and communities; neglecting it can mean spiraling costs for health care. As the cost of health care continues to increase, disease prevention, health promotion, and access to services are assuming greater importance in the public health agenda.

Recent increases in the incidence of several easily preventable diseases, such as measles and mumps, have underscored the cost-effectiveness of a prevention-oriented approach. For example, a single dose of vaccine against measles, mumps, and rubella costs approximately $25. But the cost of not being vaccinated can be staggering. Complications from measles can result in death or blindness, mumps can leave males sterile, and rubella infection in pregnant women can seriously compromise their pregnancies. Clearly, the cost of prevention is far less than the cost to treat those diseases and their complications.

Prevention and collaboration to ensure adequate access to services while avoiding duplication of services have become fundamental components of health policy and health-care reform nationally and statewide. One indication of those trends is the movement toward school-linked services, such as after-school child-care and recreation programs.

For example, California's Healthy Start Initiative (Senate Bill 620/1991) provides funds for schools and community public and private organizations to work together to provide a system of comprehensive, integrated health, psychosocial, and educational services. The school-linked services initiative promotes the reconfiguration of existing community resources. A center at or near the school site serves as the gateway for a continuum of services (such as primary health care, mental-health services, academic support, counseling, parenting education, nutrition services, health education, youth development, or substance-abuse prevention) for students and families who need assistance.

Some services are offered on site. Others are offered through referral from the center's family advocate to a provider in the community. Services are family-focused and prevention- and result-oriented. School-linked services help ensure that existing community resources are used effectively by individuals and families who need assistance. Ongoing collaboration and consultation among school personnel, parents, and service providers results in more efficient and supportive delivery of services. Teachers are able to refer families to needed assistance and community agency staff can target services to families who want help. Together, the school, the school-linked service providers, and the family

School systems are not responsible for meeting every need of their students. But where the need directly affects learning, the school must meet the challenge. So it is with health.

—Turning Points: Preparing American Youth for the 21st Century

13

provide consistent efforts to the support the student's success at school. (See Appendix B for an example of school-linked services.)

Structures for a Comprehensive School Health System

For health education to be made meaningful, systems must be in place that support effective health education and make health an important priority in the school.

Preventing health problems, promoting health literacy, and supporting students' success at school through a comprehensive, collaborative approach may involve significant changes at some schools. However, working with families and the community, schools can establish an effective system for preventing health problems and promoting health literacy.

This framework envisions a comprehensive school health system based on the assumption, strongly supported by research and practice, that the teaching of health information alone is insufficient for children and youths to achieve health literacy. Effective health education must combine scientifically based information with approaches that develop positive health attitudes and behaviors and incorporate a wide range of learning styles, activities, and teaching strategies. It engages children on many different levels to develop knowledge, skills, attitudes, and behaviors that will make health education not the presentation of a set of facts to be studied, memorized, and quickly forgotten but a meaningful part of children's lives. In addition, it relates health information to a variety of disciplines and learning situations.

For health education to be made meaningful, systems must be in place that support effective health education and make health an important priority in the school. The school's approach must be well planned, must be coherent, must be implemented consistently, and must be supported by all adults in the school. All the components of the school's program must be mutually supportive and consistent with the overall goal of promoting and enhancing children's health literacy.

This schoolwide approach is referred to in this framework as a *comprehensive school health system* with eight components:

- Health Education
- Physical Education
- Nutrition Services
- Health Services
- Psychological and Counseling Services
- Safe and Healthy School Environment
- Health Promotion for Staff
- Parent and Community Involvement[12]

These eight components work together to develop and reinforce health-related knowledge, skills, attitudes, and behaviors and make health an important priority at the school. The components are linked in a mutually supportive, cooperative system focusing on children's health issues and the development of health literacy. Each of the eight components is a critical link in the overall support system for school health and is integrally related to the other components. Some of the components focus on education, others on services, and still others on the school environment. When they are planned and implemented in a supportive and consistent manner, the eight components achieve far more in promoting health literacy than is possible without a coherent, integrated system. The entire support system is shown in Figure 1.

---

[12] The model of a comprehensive school health system described in this framework was most recently presented in the Healthy Kids, Healthy, California Initiative. For information about the initiative, contact the Healthy Kids, Healthy California Office, California Department of Education, 721 Capitol Mall, Sacramento, California (mailing address: P.O. Box 944272, Sacramento, CA 94244-2720); telephone (916) 657-2810.

Figure 1

A Comprehensive School Health System

Health Education

Parent/Community
Involvement

Physical Education

Health Promotion
for Staff

Health Services

Healthy School
Environment

Nutrition Services

Psychological
and Counseling
Services

- *Health education and physical education* focus on helping students gain the knowledge, skills, and behaviors needed for health literacy and on engendering the attitudes they also need for lifelong healthy behaviors. Health education is the primary focus of this framework. Physical education taught within the context of a comprehensive school health system is the subject of its own framework. Readers seeking detailed information about the design of exemplary physical education curriculum should consult the *Physical Education Framework*.

- *Health services, nutrition services, and psychological and counseling services* reinforce the knowledge, skills, and behaviors taught in health education and physical education; help families support and promote students' health; and provide students with opportunities to practice healthy behaviors. For example, school nutrition services support healthy growth and development by providing nutritious foods to students. School nutrition services also offer students opportunities to apply knowledge of nutrition learned in the classroom to their selection of nutritious foods at school.

Health services, including early and periodic health screenings, such as examinations of vision and hearing, provided at or near the school site offer students access to vital health care that is often not available to them from any other source. Psychological and counseling services provided at or near the school site offer students assistance and support in making healthy decisions, coping with crises, and resolving or managing problems that might influence success at school. When provided in the context of a comprehensive school health system, these types of services can also

The components of a comprehensive school health system are linked in a mutually supportive, cooperative system focusing on children's health issues and the development of health literacy.

help students and their families find the support they need in a coordinated and effective manner.

- *Safe and healthy school environment, health promotion for staff, and parent and community involvement* all support and reinforce the school's commitment to the development of health literacy. A safe and healthy school environment ensures that students and adults at the school site are physically safe and that the school environment supports health literacy and successful learning. Health promotion for staff empowers teachers and other staff members to make a commitment to lifelong healthy behaviors and model those behaviors for students. In addition, parent and community involvement brings parents, the community, and the school together to develop and support health literacy. As a result the school views itself as an integral part of the community and works in partnership with parents to promote the success of students.

Parents and the community are involved in a variety of roles in the school, ranging from occasional volunteering to active, meaningful leadership on school committees. Parent and community involvement, health promotion for staff, and a safe and healthy school environment all contribute to developing a schoolwide commitment to health. Each of these components should be developed and supported as a necessary part of the comprehensive school health system. Together, the components of a comprehensive school health system empower students to develop and apply knowledge and skills leading to healthy choices and lifelong good health. This system provides the school and community with a sound approach for preventing health problems when possible and dealing with them in a systematic way when they do occur. When a well-designed curriculum and a supporting structure are available, the goal of health literacy for all children is realistic and achievable.

When a well-designed curriculum and a supporting structure are available, the goal of health literacy for all children is realistic and achievable.

Parents as Providers and Decision Makers

Parents and guardians should be closely involved in the design and implementation of efforts to support children's health from the very beginning of the process. This involvement should go well beyond token participation.

Why is it important to involve parents? First, it helps to keep the planning and implementation of the comprehensive school health system on the right track. As experts on their children and on their own communities, parents can ensure that schools address the issues that families and communities perceive as relevant. Second, active participation is in itself an intervention for the individual parents who get involved. Providing individuals with opportunities to be connected, to grow and develop, and to give back to their community allows them to see new possibilities for themselves. Third, involving parents builds the community's capacity for self-sufficiency. Community members learn to do for themselves and each other, rather than wait for an outside person or group to provide for them or to lead them. Fourth, community parents can bring valuable assets to family outreach work, including a knowledge of different community cultures and languages, an ability, as peers, to build close and trusting relationships quickly, and an ability to identify unique solutions to problems that professionals might not see.

Therefore, schools should involve parents in developing and providing support activities, such as organizing transportation, following up with tardy children in the neighborhood each morning, overseeing an after-school study club, organizing parent support groups on various topics, fund-raising for small projects, and so on. Schools may also consider involving parents in more paraprofessional types of support, such as individual peer counseling or case management. When parents will be filling paraprofessional roles, the school must provide parents with the necessary training in maintaining confidentiality, keeping records, conducting interviews and so forth.

Parents and guardians should also be key decision makers on policy issues and should be represented in sufficient numbers to have an impact. Parents should be involved in all decisions that will affect them, especially on such matters as which services are to be offered to families and how services should be adapted to make them culturally meaningful.

Chapter 2

Developing Health Literacy in the Classroom and in the School

How can schools foster health literacy in all students? This chapter contains suggestions on how schools can deliver quality health education within the context of a comprehensive school health system. Although there are many ways to design and implement an effective school health system, this chapter is meant to be a starting point, a guide that schools and school districts can use in creating their own system and overall strategy to promote health literacy. It contains two sections, one focusing on elements of successful health education, the other on effective implementation of a comprehensive school health system.

Elements of Successful Health Education

To help students develop the knowledge, skills, attitudes, and behaviors needed for a lifelong commitment to health, effective health education:

- *Presents current, accurate content.* All health-related education is based on up-to-date scientific information. It draws on new knowledge about health and maintains a rigorous scientific viewpoint.

- *Recognizes similarities and differences among students.* Effective health education emphasizes the similarities and universal qualities of human beings, helping students see that although differences do exist, many people face similar health-related issues and choices. Regardless of differences in age, culture, disability, ethnic background, gender, primary language, religion, sexual orientation, or socioeconomic background, the students must understand that the knowledge, skills, and behaviors discussed in class apply to all students. Differences should also be discussed, but care should be taken not to emphasize them to the point of divisiveness.

- *Emphasizes not just health-related information but the importance of behavior.* Information alone does not change people's behavior. A lifelong commitment to health results from knowledge, skills, attitudes, and positive behaviors continually repeated and reinforced. Focusing on behavior involves providing students with opportunities to learn, practice, and apply new skills, such as making decisions, refusing negative influences, and accessing health and social service programs to maintain good

Curriculum reform has several important ramifications for teachers. . . . Teachers have to redesign their courses for a higher level of student work and use methods that enable more students to succeed at this level.

—Second to None: A Vision of the New California High School

22

health. Seen in this way, effective health education does not limit itself to the pages of a textbook but views the school as a safe laboratory for learning, practicing, and reinforcing new behaviors.

- *Is culturally appropriate.* Attitudes, beliefs, and values regarding health-related topics may vary according to the ethnic and cultural makeup of the community. Effective health education should be based on an awareness of the culture and background of students within each classroom and the influence of culture on the information and skills to be taught. Such an awareness will affect the teaching strategies used and the content of the curriculum. For example, many health education programs teach students how to be assertive and resist negative influences. Yet in some cultures young people are expected to be quiet and obedient, and in other cultures public discussion of certain health-related topics may be considered inappropriate. Whatever the approach, the cultural attitudes and values of the students, their families, and the community must be taken into account.

- *Makes the curriculum accessible.* Not all students learn in the same way, nor are they motivated by the same factors. Therefore, a variety of teaching strategies, both teacher-directed and student-centered, should be used in health education. Activities should provide students with a common experiential base. A variety of grouping strategies allowing students to work individually, in pairs, in small cooperative groups, and in large groups should be used. Instruction should be provided through the primary language and sheltered English whenever possible to make the curriculum accessible to limited-English-proficient (LEP) stu-

E ffective health education should be based on an awareness of the culture and background of students within each classroom.

23

dents. Grouping students to ensure that LEP students have access to bilingual peers, making instructional resources available in the home language, and connecting instruction to students' life experiences will also promote access to the curriculum.

- *Takes advantage of opportunities for active learning.* Every aspect of health education focuses on behaviors or choices, and every topic presents opportunities for engagement and motivation. An effective health education curriculum considers students' needs, appeals to their interests, and capitalizes on those interests in many different ways. It offers abundant opportunities for critical thinking and analysis and remains focused on helping students develop a deep understanding of health literacy. It also provides students with many opportunities to be engaged in creating and constructing what they learn rather than in passively receiving factual information. Students may practice specific skills in the classroom, report on school and community resources for health, and complete meaningful, open-ended homework assignments and large projects that help connect classroom instruction with the home and the community. Classrooms, school cafeterias, nurses' offices, and school-linked community organizations, such as after-school recreation programs or organizations sponsoring community-service projects, should all become laboratories for health-related experiences.

- *Focuses on mental and emotional health throughout.* At one time mental and emotional health was viewed as a separate content area. Increasingly, however, mental and emotional health is considered crucial to an individual's motivation to act on health-related knowledge and use health-related skills. Accordingly, concepts related to mental and emotional health are discussed throughout this framework. They are basic to all

ffective health education emphasizes how ideas are connected within the curriculum and with other aspects of the overall school program.

24

of health education and are not an independent component that can be covered in a short unit and ignored in the rest of the curriculum.

- *Emphasizes character development.* Health education can promote character development. Through the health education curriculum, students learn strategies for making positive, healthy decisions based on such ethical principles as integrity, courage, responsibility, and commitment. They learn about the importance of consistent choices in all areas of their lives and how those choices affect their health and the health of others. Throughout the health education curriculum, moreover, the development of positive commitments to one's own health and the health of the broader community and society is emphasized.

- *Uses technology to enhance learning.* Technology should be made an integral element of health education. In the classroom students can use technology-based resources to practice skills (e.g., decision making). By using nutrient analysis software, students can assess how the nutritional values of choices for their own meals compare with nutritional standards. They can also develop a personal health profile that tells them where they stand in relation to group norms on a variety of health indicators such as weight and allows them to set and monitor progress toward achieving goals for improvement. In some communities students may have an opportunity to learn to operate analytical instruments used in medical laboratories, in laboratories monitoring environmental conditions, and in clinics and hospitals. Technology can also assist educators. It can help them keep pace with the rapidly changing field of health information; provide network exchanges of instructional programs, resources, services, and research articles; and access resources outside the school and the school district.

Through the health education curriculum, students learn strategies for making positive, healthy decisions based on such ethical principles as integrity, courage, responsibility, and commitment.

- *Focuses on meaning and thinking by connecting concepts in health education with other learning and experiences.* Children learn best when the curriculum is focused on meaning and thinking. Effective health education emphasizes how ideas are connected within the curriculum and with other aspects of the overall school program:

  1. *Connections with other areas of health education.* Effective health education highlights the connections among traditional health topics so that students can explore interrelationships in health. For example, individual growth and development are influenced by nutrition; personal health habits can affect the spread of communicable diseases; and the use of alcohol, tobacco, or other drugs increases the risk of disease and injury.

  2. *Connections with the other components of a comprehensive school health system.* Effective health education also links the health curriculum and the other components of a comprehensive school health system so that knowledge and skills learned in the classroom are supported and reinforced throughout the school. For example, the importance of physical fitness in health promotion and disease prevention can be reinforced and enhanced in the physical education class. Further suggestions for connecting the components of a comprehensive school health system can be found in Chapter 4.

  3. *Connections between health education and other academic disciplines.* Making connections between health education and other disciplines can enhance learning in health education and the other curriculum areas. For example, the study of nutrition and mathematics can be enhanced when students use mathematical skills in determining the calories a person needs on the basis of healthy weight and energy expenditure. Or health,

science, and language arts concepts can be woven into lessons involving biographies of great healers and scientists. Further, health education concepts can be sequenced and articulated with home economics and health careers courses. More suggestions for integrating health concepts and skills across the curriculum can be found in Chapter 5.

Two notes of caution are in order here. First, integration of health-related content should not be considered an alternative to a well-planned, sequential health education program based on clearly defined goals and outcomes. A quality health education curriculum results when attention is given to integration and articulation during program design and development. Second, because parental notification is legally mandated before a discussion of human reproductive organs may occur, schools may wish to limit integration of sex education with other topics.

With these principles of effective health education in place, a foundation can be laid for promoting health literacy and life-long healthy behaviors. However, health education alone is not enough to promote health literacy in children. Health-related knowledge, skills, attitudes, and behaviors need to be reinforced and supported. The supportive, collaborative structure needed to achieve health literacy can be provided by a comprehensive school health system.

Effective Implementation

Having all the components of a comprehensive school health system in place will take time and require careful planning. The approaches that have proven successful for program organization and implementation are as follows:

- *Create a common vision.* Although many factors contribute to an effective comprehensive school health system, none is more critical than a vision shared by the school and its parents and community. The development of that vision provides a forum for the school and all facets of the community to examine their roles in implementing a comprehensive school health system. Once developed, the vision becomes a unifying force for decision making and system development. It should include clearly defined goals and outcomes for all the components of a comprehensive school health system.

- *Provide strong administrative support.* The commitment of school and school district leaders is the key to building an effective program. One good way to start is for the school board to develop and adopt a policy clearly stating its commitment and supporting the eight components of a comprehensive school health system (see pages 30–31). Specific district policies may already offer guidance on such health matters as dispensing medication, such as that for asthma, providing school nutrition services, or dealing with HIV-infected students. These supporting policies can be reviewed for their consistency in furthering the overall goals and be revised as needed. Because the most effective policies are those that cover all issues surrounding health and contain enforcement procedures as well, school districts may choose to combine existing health policies into one comprehensive policy that contains the vision, goals, and policies and procedures for implementation and enforcement.

- *Ensure sufficient time for health education.* Because the goal of health education is to influence stu-

---

W hat makes the difference in a healthy school is that all the people who can have an impact on children's health—administrators, teachers, physical educators, nurses, counselors, support staff, food services staff, family members, community service providers, law enforcement representatives—take time to sit down together and talk about how they can work cooperatively and collaboratively to make the most of the resources available to them.

—*Toward Healthy Schools: The Future Is Now*

dents' lifelong health-related behavior, the commitment of a realistic amount of time for health education is essential. Studies have shown that when students receive instruction in health education over several years, their health-related behavior is influenced positively and significantly. Health education should begin before kindergarten and be continued yearly from kindergarten through grade twelve.

Several national research studies suggest that significant changes in knowledge about health and attitudes toward health seem to occur after 50 hours of classroom instruction per school year or about one and one-half hours per week.[1] This framework recommends that the kindergarten through grade twelve course of study in health be anchored by a full year's work at the middle school level and a second full year's work at the high school level. Various options exist for including health education in the curriculum at those levels, and decisions on how best to offer health education should be made locally. What is essential is that adequate amounts of time be allocated for such instruction.

- *Encourage broad-based involvement.* Broad-based involvement is crucial to developing and maintaining articulated kindergarten through grade twelve health education and instituting a comprehensive school health system. Many individuals can be involved in a schoolwide effort. Effective strategies for creating involvement include the following:

    1. *Forming a school-site health team or health committee.* This group can have responsibility for guiding the process, including planning, coordinating parent

his framework recommends that the kindergarten through grade twelve course of study in health be anchored by a full year's work at the middle school level and a second full year's work at the high school level.

---

[1]D. Connell and others, "Summary of Findings of the School Health Education Evaluation: Health Promotion Effectiveness, Implementation, and Costs," *Journal of School Health*, Vol. 55, No. 8 (1985), 316–21.

School Policies on Health Issues

A clearly stated policy that defines the comprehensive school health system and expresses support for this system can greatly facilitate effective implementation. Specific district policies on a variety of health-related issues can be reviewed for their consistency with the comprehensive school health system and incorporated into this policy. Addressing all health issues in one board policy helps ensure consistency and facilitates review and revision when necessary.

Districts developing policies for the first time or districts updating policies may wish to consider the California State Board of Education's policy on nutrition and state law regarding tobacco-free policies. These policies are summarized below:

Policy on Nutrition

The State Board of Education recommends that local educational agency and county office governing boards adopt policies that address all of the following issues:

1. A statement summarizing the district's or county office's nutrition policy

2. A plan for policy implementation and enforcement

3. A description of the local enforcement procedure

The policy should apply to all school-approved groups, including but not limited to students, teachers, parents, booster groups, and outside vendors. It would be appropriate for elementary school policies to be more restrictive than those for junior and senior high schools. Local policies that are more restrictive than existing state or federal laws and regulations are also acceptable.

Tobacco-free Policies

"All school districts and county offices of education . . . shall adopt smoke-free campus policies and shall prohibit the use of tobacco on school property no later than July 1, 1996" (*Health and Safety Code* Section 24167[q][2]). A fully implemented tobacco-free policy includes the following:

• Policy prohibits the use of tobacco products anywhere, anytime on county or district property and in county or district vehicles.

• Enforcement procedures are established.

• Information about the policy and enforcement procedures are communicated clearly to county, district, or school personnel, parents, students, and the larger community.

• Signs stating the prohibition of tobacco use are prominently displayed at all entrances to county, district, or school property.

• A referral program to smoking cessation support programs is made available, and students and staff are encouraged to participate.

and community involvement, developing curriculum, and implementing program components consistently. Membership should be representative of the entire school: classroom teachers; teachers of health education, physical education, home economics, science, and special education; school nurses; counselors; school nutrition services personnel; categorical program staff; administrators; others at the school site; parents; and community members. School-linked service providers, such as social workers, child-care providers, recreation specialists, probation officers, and others, may also be included.

2. *Fostering parent and community involvement.* Parent and community involvement is discussed in more detail in Chapter 4 as one component of a comprehensive school health system. However, it is important to note here that strong ties to the community will enhance the school's efforts to promote health literacy. The process of developing a consensus about community needs and wants regarding a comprehensive school health system should be continuing, open, and responsive.

3. *Providing mechanisms for effective coordination, collaboration, and communication.* Designating a staff member to coordinate activities and facilitate communication among the various participants helps ensure that these critical activities are handled effectively. The roles and responsibilities of a coordinator might include working with the on-site team and others to assess the school's health education curriculum; providing or arranging for in-service training of staff on health-related issues; maintaining continuing and open communication among

school staff; working with the appropriate staff to plan and implement connections between health education and other curriculum areas; organizing meetings to share information with parents and community members; writing grant proposals; monitoring the progress of the overall program; establishing clear and appropriate lines of referral between the school, parents, and community agencies; and maintaining a dialogue with county-level groups involved with services for children and youths.

- *Identify resources for program support.* Many communities are able to provide a variety of resources for a comprehensive school health system. Some of these resources (e.g., targeted funding, after-school activities, and staff who can assist with program implementation) are a response to local needs, such as gang activity or a high incidence of drug use. The organizers and coordinators of school-based programs should look to community health and human-service providers for available resources and find ways to create linkages between those resources and the school.

Such linkages can enhance an effective comprehensive school health system. Only through the collaborative efforts of school personnel, parents, and community agencies and representatives will most schools be able to assist students and their families in obtaining needed health, mental health, social, and other support services, ranging from basic food, clothing, and housing programs to child-care and recreational programs. These community linkages can also enrich health education by offering real-life experiences to students through health-related issues, practices, and programs.

- *Provide adequate training.* Different kinds of training and different approaches for diverse audiences will be needed as the school's comprehensive school health system unfolds, including the following:

  1. *Teacher training.* High-quality staff development, a key factor in effective education, is especially needed for health education. The teacher must have a good understanding of the content, a sensitivity to and enthusiasm for nurturing the health of each student, and an ability and willingness to model healthy living. New teachers, including all elementary teachers, must be adequately prepared to teach this area of the curriculum by taking an accredited university course dealing with teaching health education. High school teachers who teach a specific health class or who teach health as part of a home economics or science course also need special preservice preparation and training.

     In addition, all those teaching health need continuing professional development opportunities so that they can maintain their knowledge of current health topics and successful instructional strategies. Each district should ensure that teachers have sufficient opportunities for professional development in health education.

  2. *Training for other staff.* Nonteaching staff at the school, such as secretaries, school maintenance personnel, and classroom assistants, interact with and influence young people. The

Project TEACH
(Teacher Education to Achieve Comprehensive Health), funded by California College Health 2000 and the California Department of Education, was designed to strengthen and unify the health education class required during teacher preservice training in California.
(See Appendix C.)

entire staff should be offered training in the philosophy of the comprehensive school health system and their roles in helping students develop lifelong healthy behaviors. In addition, opportunities for cross-training with school-linked health and human-services providers will greatly strengthen the comprehensive school health system. Training of this type is consistent with and may be a part of efforts to restructure schools. The major California school reform documents (*Here They Come: Ready or Not; It's Elementary; Caught in the Middle;* and *Second to None*) challenge schools to look at the entire curriculum and the environment of the school to ensure that all students succeed. Involvement of staff members in the comprehensive school health system supports that goal.

3. *Training and informational presentations for parents*. Parents should be offered opportunities to learn more about the content of the health education curriculum and the philosophy behind the comprehensive school health system. They should understand the range of topics in the curriculum and should also have access to content.

- *Keep the vision in focus*. Once there is commitment to the vision and broad-based input, planning for further implementation of the components of a comprehensive school health system should be a continuing process. Developing, evaluating, and refining specific goals and objectives for the comprehensive school health system will ensure that the vision remains at the heart of the effort. Many schools will have some components of a

All staff and parents should be offered training in the philosophy of the comprehensive school health system and their roles in helping students develop lifelong healthy behaviors.

35

Meeting these challenges is the only wise course toward securing the future of the nation. But more than that, it is the right and moral thing to do for our young people, and we must accept nothing less.

—Code Blue: Uniting for Healthier Youth

comprehensive school health system already in place and functioning well, others will be in place but in need of change, and still others will not yet be under way. Strategic thinking and planning will be needed, but the vision of a comprehensive approach will be the essential guide.

A quality health education curriculum supported by the components of a comprehensive school health system with high visibility, effective monitoring, and qualified and enthusiastic participants is not an impossible goal. Although planning and implementation will take time and thoughtful effort, a comprehensive school health system can be achieved when families, communities, and schools work together and make the health of children and youths a priority.

Chapter 3

Health Education

I. The Health Curriculum: An Overview

Health education is integral to a comprehensive school health system. A well-designed health curriculum for students in kindergarten through grade twelve offers abundant opportunities for engaging students and involving them in meaningful learning experiences. The curriculum should provide students with opportunities to explore concepts in depth, analyze and solve real-life problems, and work cooperatively on tasks that develop and enhance their conceptual understanding. It also provides students with the knowledge and skills that can lead to lifelong positive attitudes and behaviors related to health.

The major goal of health education envisioned in this framework is the development of health literacy in all students. The four unifying ideas of health literacy emphasized throughout the health curriculum are the following:

- *Acceptance of personal responsibility*, including responsibility for personal lifelong health, acceptance of the idea that the individual has some control over health, and incorporation of health-related knowledge into everyday behavior

- *Respect for and promotion of the health of others*, including an understanding and acceptance of the influence of behavior on the health and well-being of others, of people on the environment, and of the environment on the health of groups and individuals

- *An understanding of the process of growth and development*, including the importance of both universal and individual aspects of physical, mental, emotional, and social growth and development

- *Informed use of health-related information, products, and services*, including the ability to select and use health-related information, products, and services carefully and wisely

A curriculum that addresses the four unifying ideas will draw content from the nine major content areas of health education:

- Personal Health
- Consumer and Community Health
- Injury Prevention and Safety
- Alcohol, Tobacco, and Other Drugs
- Nutrition
- Environmental Health
- Family Living

- Individual Growth and Development

- Communicable and Chronic Diseases

The content areas are the traditional, widely used subject categories of health education. With minor variations they have appeared consistently in previous California frameworks and in other state and national descriptions of comprehensive health education. Together, the content areas describe the range of health concepts, skills, and behaviors important for today's students. In the course of a year, most if not all of the content areas should be included in the curriculum. To be woven throughout the content areas are the concepts related to mental and emotional health. Basic to all parts of health education, those concepts are to be included in the curriculum each year.

The content areas are not distinct from the four unifying ideas of health literacy. Rather, the unifying ideas run through and connect the content areas in a student-centered approach that makes instruction meaningful to students. A well-designed health curriculum combines the four unifying ideas with the content areas in a continuing spiral of knowledge and skill development from kindergarten through grade twelve. This chapter presents the broad outlines of such a program.

II. Content Areas, Kindergarten Through Grade Twelve

The following descriptions of the nine content areas apply across grade levels from kindergarten through grade twelve. Expectations and content for specific ranges of grade levels can be found in Section III.

Personal Health

Personal health lays the foundation for good general health. Instruction in personal health encourages a positive commitment to health and well-being rooted in respect for oneself and one's physical, mental, emotional, and social health. Understanding that exercise is essential to good health, a person realizes that to stay healthy and fit is basic to personal health.

Three ideas are central to personal health. First, good health is not simply a matter of luck or accident; it involves taking responsibility and making deliberate choices. Second, good health involves an interaction of physical, mental, emotional, and social aspects of health, reflecting the interdependence of body and mind. Third, a commitment to personal health is one basis for leading a happy, healthy, productive life.

Consumer and Community Health

As a nation we face a growing concern about the cost of health care and the need to focus on health promotion and disease prevention. Addressing that concern implies a shift not only in how health-care services are provided but also in how individuals take an active role in deciding on their use of health-care services and health-related products.

Three main ideas are central to this content area. First, the age-old principle of buyer beware is particularly relevant to health-related decisions. In many cases medical problems may get better without treatment or with simple treatment at home. When skilled health care is needed, one should know how to find the appropriate services and avoid products or services that may be useless or even harmful. Second, preventing illness and promoting health are in the best interest of both individuals and society. Third, a variety of community organizations and agencies are available to assist those experiencing problems.

Injury Prevention and Safety

However childhood injury is measured (in number of deaths, dollar costs for treatment, relative rankings with other health problems, or loss of potential years of life), it ranks first among health problems affecting children in California and the nation. Historically, although childhood mortality due to disease has been reduced dramatically, that due to injury has increased steadily. Unintentional injuries, mainly those involving motor vehicles but also those caused by drowning, fire, suffocation, or poisoning, together with intentional injuries resulting from violent behavior, rank among the greatest threats to the health of children and young adults.

Yet the causes of injuries can be prevented or avoided. This content area focuses on prevention through safe living habits and positive, healthy decisions. Simple precautions and an awareness of the consequences of one's choices and decisions can help to prevent many unintentional injuries. This content area also acknowledges that violence is a public health issue. The curriculum at all grade levels should include a comprehensive approach to the prevention of violence.

Another focus of this content area is knowing what to do when confronted with emergencies. Appropriate responses are critically important in emergencies resulting from natural disasters or the actions of dangerous persons.

Note: See *Education Code* Section 51202 (instruction in personal and public health and safety) in Appendix A. The requirements of this code section should be understood prior to the development of curriculum in this content area.

Violence is a public health issue. The curriculum at all grade levels should include a comprehensive approach to the prevention of violence.

Alcohol, Tobacco, and Other Drugs

The use of alcohol, tobacco, and other drugs, so pervasive and so potentially damaging to the health of individuals and society, has major implications in the lifelong health of individuals. Successful efforts to prevent the use of tobacco are effective against four of the five leading causes of death in California: heart disease, cancer, chronic obstructive lung disease, and fire caused by smoking.

A multifaceted approach, including a full range of prevention and intervention components, is required to safeguard the health of students from the effects of alcohol, tobacco, and other drugs. As a starting point information should be presented on the effects of alcohol, tobacco, including smokeless tobacco and secondhand smoke, and other drugs on the body. Information should also be presented on all types of drugs, including medicines and such performance-enhancing substances as steroids. The proper use of medication and the role of medication in the treatment of disease are key concepts. The effects of alcohol, tobacco, and other drugs on pregnant women and their children should also be addressed, together with the social effects of their use and the relation of alcohol and drug use to suicide, violence, and other health and safety issues.

As important as the development of knowledge related to alcohol, tobacco, and other drugs is the need for young people to develop skills in resisting the influence of peers and the media to use legal and illegal substances that are potentially harmful. With so many health-related choices influenced by peers, skill-building activities, such as development of refusal and communication skills, are a necessary component of instruction at all grade levels. Students should know that the consumption of alcohol and the use of tobacco and other drugs (with the exception of appropriate medications) are prohibited at school and should be familiar with the consequences for failure to comply.

A multifaceted approach, including a full range of prevention and intervention components, is required to safeguard the health of students from the effects of alcohol, tobacco, and other drugs.

The environment in which alcohol, tobacco, and other drugs are made available must also be considered. Society accepts the adult use of tobacco and alcohol, sending conflicting messages to young people regarding their use. As a result children must be prepared to deal with situations in which they cannot control the use of alcohol, tobacco, and other drugs by others. To strengthen the school's message and provide for consistency at home and in the community, parents and other members of the community should be involved in developing curriculum and intervention strategies designed to prevent the use of alcohol, tobacco, and other drugs and should be encouraged to support the school's no-use message to students. They should work together to identify and reduce specific risks and increase protection.

Collaborative efforts are also helpful in refining and enhancing procedures for identification, assessment, referral, and ongoing support for children and youths who have previously used alcohol, tobacco, or other drugs and in providing information on available counseling, treatment, and reentry programs and services to students and employees. One important, appropriate function of community involvement is communicating information to parents and the community about problems with the use of alcohol, tobacco, and other drugs experienced by youths as well as effective strategies to prevent their use. In addition, community involvement brings law enforcement agencies and the community into the schools, builds bridges between the school and the community, and develops more effective communication and cooperative relationships. Through a well-coordinated effort, schools, families, law enforcement agencies, and the community can work together to develop, promote, and carry out a clear, unified position on the use of alcohol, tobacco, and other drugs.

Note: See *Education Code* sections 51202 (instruction on personal and public health and safety) and 51203 (instruction on alcohol, narcotics, and restricted dangerous drugs) in Appendix A. The requirements of these code sections should be understood prior to the development of curriculum in this content area.

Drug, Alcohol, and Tobacco Education Application

The Drug, Alcohol, and Tobacco Education (DATE) application represents a collaborative effort by the California Department of Education, school districts, and county offices of education to provide a comprehensive approach to alcohol, tobacco, and drug use prevention and intervention programs. The DATE application requires descriptions of the following components:

1. **Planning process,** including a needs assessment and evidence of a comprehensive, collaborative approach to planning that includes those individuals and organizations specified in the legislation, such as school representatives, parents, community groups, law enforcement representatives, citizens, and public health representatives

2. **School policy,** including policies and regulations that address prevention, intervention, and enforcement procedures

3. **In-service training,** including in-service and professional development training directed at school staff, parents, and community groups and agencies

4. **Curriculum,** including how an integrated and comprehensive alcohol, tobacco, and other drug use prevention curriculum containing a clear "no-use" message is being implemented at every grade level, kindergarten through grade twelve

5. **Intervention,** including identification, intervention, and referral services

6. **Parent education/involvement,** including how parents are directly involved in alcohol, tobacco, and other drug-use prevention programs and training in awareness, intervention, positive parenting, and referral services

7. **Community involvement,** including how the community and community agencies are involved in developing and implementing a plan to prevent drug, alcohol, and tobacco use by youths and are working collaboratively with schools to provide prevention and intervention services

8. **Positive alternatives,** including how students will be offered a variety of opportunities to become involved in activities and events that promote a life-style which is free of tobacco, alcohol, and other drugs

9. **Evaluation,** including how feedback about successes and failures will be provided and incorporated into the planning component

Adapted from the 1993-94 DATE application.

Nutrition

To be ready to learn and to achieve their fullest potential, children need to be well nourished and healthy. For that reason they must have an adequate supply of healthy foods and the knowledge and skills required to make wise food choices. A primary issue for all children, then, especially the increasing number of children living in poverty, is access to an adequate diet. Effective nutrition education provides children and their families with information on gaining access to adequate food sources, including the range of school nutrition programs available.

The link between nutrition and good health or, conversely, between poor nutrition and illness is another key concept. Healthy eating habits and an active life-style can increase resistance to communicable diseases and reduce the risk of chronic disease, developmental disabilities, and infant mortality, a particularly serious problem of teenage pregnancy. In California the basis for nutrition recommendations is the *California Daily Food Guide*,[1] which incorporates the federal dietary guidelines for Americans and the dietary recommendations of other national health authorities. Current nutrition recommendations are illustrated in the food guide pyramid developed by the U.S. Department of Agriculture.

Students learn that food choices are intimately linked with physical, mental, emotional, and social health; energy level; self-image; and physical fitness. This content area provides students with the knowledge, skills, and motivation needed to make wise food choices throughout their lives. Ideally, nutrition education uses the school's child nutrition programs as an essential part of the educational process. Food-tasting and preparation experiences at all grade levels can provide an excellent opportunity for classroom teachers to work cooperatively with school nutrition personnel and use the cafeteria as a learning laboratory for classroom lessons as required by fed-

---

[1]*The California Daily Food Guide.* Developed by the California Department of Health Services in collaboration with the California Department of Aging and the California Department of Education. Sacramento: California Department of Education, 1990. Ordering information can be found at the back of this publication.

Nutrition Services Specialists:
Resources for Health Education

Often overlooked as health education or program resources are the professional nutritionists and registered dietitians affiliated with child nutrition programs. These nutrition specialists can provide tremendous resources. They and other child nutrition staff can help augment classroom activities and assist teachers with the integration of nutrition- or food-related activities with many subject areas and various schoolwide programs and services. Examples of such activities include:

- Providing assistance with mathematical calculations of the nutritional values of foods, recipes, and menus

- Developing consumer education skills, such as reading labels and getting the most for students' food dollars

- Increasing respect for other cultures and the foods of those cultures

- Providing assistance with lessons on the chemical reactions that take place in foods and lessons on safe food-handling practices and the relationship between food-handling and microbiology

- Providing assistance in developing disaster-preparedness plans and food kits for students

- Providing parent education in nutrition and food-related consumer practices

- Addressing the nutritional concerns of students with special health conditions

By including child nutrition professionals in programs and services, districts can maximize their resources and make the health team more comprehensive.

eral and state legislation. (Public Law 95-166 provides funds to states for the development of comprehensive nutrition education programs that make full use of the school cafeteria.) One model nutrition curriculum is contained in the California Department of Education's *Choose Well, Be Well* series.[2]

Environmental
Health

The primary focus of this content area is to make students aware of how environmental issues affect their personal health. The content area also suggests specific steps that students can take as individuals and citizens to protect and improve the environment.

A number of health conditions are either caused or exacerbated by environmental factors. For example, asthma and other lung ailments can be aggravated by air pollutants; skin cancer, by unprotected exposure to the sun; intestinal disorders, by polluted water; and allergies, by pollens, dust, or animal dander. In addition, environmental teratogens, both naturally occurring and synthetic, can cause birth defects and developmental disabilities. Health hazards from air pollution, water pollution, excessive noise levels, unprotected sun exposure, and unhealthy working or living conditions are also unfortunate features of modern life.

Students need to learn about health hazards resulting from the environment. They also need to be taught about the precautions and behaviors they can practice to safeguard their health from environmental hazards. This awareness should be combined with an awareness of practices that will reverse or at least slow down environmental pollution and related problems. Lessons that relate to recycling, conservation of re-

---

[2]*Choose Well, Be Well* is a series of nutrition curriculum materials designed by teachers and nutrition experts for students in preschool through grade twelve. Titles and ordering information can be found at the back of this publication.

sources, and an appreciation of the finite limits of environmental resources are important in this content area.

Note: See *Education Code* sections 51202 (instruction in personal and public health and safety) in Appendix A. The requirement of this code section should be understood prior to the development of curriculum in this content area.

Family Living

In the teaching of family living, particular attention must be paid to the legislative codes and guidelines that affect curriculum planning and instruction within this content area. *Note:* See *Education Code* sections 51550 (parent notification), 51553 (abstinence instruction), 51201.5 (HIV/AIDS prevention instruction), and 60650 (assessment) in Appendix A. The requirements of these code sections should be understood prior to the development of curriculum in this content area.

A functional family unit is vital to the well-being of children. Children usually develop best when they live in a stable environment with their mother and father and receive from their parents consistent love, support, and direction. However, children from nontraditional families can also develop successfully. Given the variety of nontraditional families in contemporary society, it is important that children not reared in two-parent families be convinced that their situation can also be conducive to growth and development.

Further, it is important that children not be denigrated because of their living arrangement or the composition of their family. All students, regardless of their current living arrangement, can benefit from classroom instruction and discussion on family living. They can learn how they can contribute to making the family unit harmonious and successful now as well as in the future—when they will likely become parents.

This content area promotes the development of positive family interactions in all types of families, including those that face unusual challenges. Families that have members with physical or mental disabilities can experience major effects on patterns of family interaction. Ideally, families can adapt to these challenges and in fact may develop stronger, more supportive family relationships as a result. Members of these families should feel comfortable participating in classroom discussions of family interactions.

Instruction in family living also focuses on sexuality, the reproductive process, dating relationships, and the selection of a mate. Abstinence from sexual activity is strongly encouraged because it is the healthiest course of action for young people. In addition, the moral, legal, and economic responsibilities of parenthood are highlighted.

Although sexually transmitted diseases relate to topics within the content area of family living, they are discussed under communicable and chronic diseases. Because parents should be the primary source of sex education and values relating to this subject, they must be notified before lessons in sex education are offered. The *Education Code* permits parents to withdraw their children from this portion of the health curriculum.

Ultimately, decisions regarding specific instruction in family living rest with school districts. A publication was developed to provide guidance to school districts in the development of sex education programs in their schools.[3] The approach of this framework and the *Family Life/Sex Education Guidelines* is to encourage districts to work with parents and community members in developing curriculum, especially in the area of family living. The intent of the curriculum in this content area is not to invade the privacy of families and their right to teach

[3]*Family Life/Sex Education Guidelines*. Adopted by the California State Board of Education. Sacramento: California Department of Education, 1987. Ordering information can be found at the back of this publication.

values to their children but to assist families in teaching about family living and encourage effective family communication.

Because of the sensitive nature of this content area, school districts may wish to arrange same-sex groupings during presentation of this portion of the curriculum to younger students. As for controversial issues, the *Family Life/Sex Education Guidelines* states that districts should work with parents and community members to " . . . decide how controversial issues such as homosexuality, abortion, contraception, and masturbation will or will not be addressed. Parents should be informed of the district's position, and teachers should receive clear training in fulfilling the district's policies."[4]

Family life curricula that deal with controversial issues should include factual, substantiated information and, if consistent with district policy, an opportunity for students to explore different aspects of controversial issues within the parameters allowed by law. The school district must determine what constitutes factual, substantiated information and ensure that all instructional resources used in the study of controversial issues are subject to the district's review and approval process. If guest speakers are invited to participate in the discussion of those issues, the speakers' activities must be made to adhere to district policy and state law. Further, districts must ensure that schools comply with all legal requirements concerning family life education, including providing written notification to parents before conducting classes in which the human reproductive organs and their functions are described, illustrated, or discussed.[5]

Sexual activity is not appropriate for young people. Working with parents, schools should examine their curriculum and policies to ensure that students develop the skills to make a commitment to abstain from sexual activity and to keep that commitment.

[4]*Family Life/Sex Education Guidelines.* Sacramento: California Department of Education, 1987, p. 28.
[5]School district governing boards dealing with policy issues should refer to pages 186–87 for more information relative to factual, substantiated information. See also pages 115 and 146.

51

Individual Growth and Development

An important element of health is our view of ourselves and our sense of our relationship to those around us. This content area provides information about the wide range of patterns and rates of physical, mental, emotional, and social development that occur among children and young adults. This information includes the stages of the life cycle from conception through death, physical changes that occur during puberty, and changes in relationships with others that accompany social development and the aging process.

This content area encourages students to take pride in their personal identity. It teaches them to view self-esteem as being based not only on one's accomplishments but also on personal values and ethical considerations. Further, self-esteem frees one to make healthy decisions and refuse to take part in negative behaviors without the fear of rejection that may inhibit some individuals.

In addition, this content area focuses on the importance of positive interpersonal relationships as an element in individual health and well-being. Friendships are essential to a feeling of belonging and self-worth. Skills for sustaining long-term friendships can be cultivated, and friends can help each other make responsible decisions.

Finally, this content area addresses the growing number of physically or mentally challenged students being mainstreamed into regular classes and promotes their acceptance. As a result of mainstreaming, more children will be exposed to classmates with serious illness and may even experience the death of a classmate. Studying this content area will help students understand and respond appropriately to students with special needs.

Communicable and Chronic Diseases

The most important message to convey in this content area is that students have a considerable measure of control over their health and that chances of contracting most illnesses can be greatly influenced by students' health-related choices and decisions. Such communicable diseases as sexually transmitted diseases (STDs), including HIV/AIDS and hepatitis B, dramatically illustrate the point. Chances of contracting these diseases are greatly reduced when young people abstain from sexual activity and intravenous drug use and use universal precautions when dealing with other people's body fluids. (*Note:* The importance of abstinence education is emphasized in the section on family living.)

Although the effects of heredity must be considered, behaviors and decisions also affect the development of such chronic diseases as cardiovascular disease, cancer, hypertension and stroke, diabetes, and osteoporosis. The risk factors for these diseases can begin to be detected early in life and are greatly influenced by health-related choices. Communicable and chronic diseases are too often the consequences of short-sighted or uninformed choices.

With so many health-related choices influenced by peers, skill-building activities, such as development of refusal and communication skills, are a necessary component of instruction at all grade levels. Physically or mentally challenged children are especially susceptible to peer pressure and should be included in skill-building instruction and practice.

This content area also includes the skills necessary to act in a supportive yet safe manner toward people with diseases. Although it is important to promote tolerance toward people with disease, individuals and society also need to work to control and eradicate disease.

The discussion of sexually transmitted diseases and HIV infection and AIDS is a necessary and important part of this

Most persons with AIDS were exposed to the human immunodeficiency virus (HIV) because they willingly participated in high-risk sexual behavior or used drugs intravenously. These behavior patterns often begin before or during adolescence. For that reason children and adolescents must be taught to practice behaviors that eliminate or reduce the risk of HIV infection.

content area. (*Note:* See *Education Code* sections 51550 (parent notification), 51553 (abstinence instruction), 51201.5 (HIV/AIDS prevention instruction), and 60650 (assessment) in Appendix A. The requirements of these code sections should be understood prior to the development of curriculum in this content area.) As with the family life content area, parents must be notified before sex education classes are offered in which the human reproductive organs and their functions are described, illustrated, or discussed, including discussion of sexually transmitted diseases. Parents may withdraw their children from this portion of the health curriculum.

The discussion of communicable and chronic diseases can be sensitive and have cultural, socioeconomic, genetic, or religious implications. Although decisions regarding curriculum content rest with school districts, the approach of this framework and the *Family Life/Sex Education Guidelines* is to encourage districts to work with parents and community members in developing the curriculum.

III. Expectations and Content, by Grade Level

Structure of the Grade-Level Instructional Guidelines

Each of the following sections introduces concepts and suggestions designed to facilitate the planning of curricula, instructional units, and instructional resources. Each section focuses on the four unifying ideas of health literacy and follows a specific format.

- Unifying idea: acceptance of personal responsibility for lifelong health; respect for and promotion of the health of others; understanding of the process of growth and development; and informed use of health-related information, products, and services

- Grade-level expectations

- Concepts and content to be emphasized

- Examples of skills and behaviors to be taught and reinforced

Kindergarten Through Grade Three

Although much of their environment and daily living activities are beyond their control, students in kindergarten through grade three can choose many behaviors that contribute to good health. Because young children tend to be unselfconsciously egocentric, a curriculum that focuses on them and on what they can do to promote their well-being captures their interest and attention. The curriculum should begin with the children and their immediate environment so that they can make clear connections to information, concepts, skills, and behaviors. It should also sustain a focus on the children's social development as members of the classroom, the school, families, and communities. Throughout, the prevention of unhealthy behaviors and promotion of attitudes and behaviors that can lead to lifelong health practices should be strongly emphasized.

Unifying Idea: Acceptance of personal responsibility for lifelong health

Expectations:

1. Students will demonstrate ways in which they can enhance and maintain their health and well-being.

2. Students will demonstrate behaviors that prevent disease and speed recovery from illness.

3. Students will practice behaviors that reduce the risk of becoming involved in potentially dangerous situations and react to potentially dangerous situations in ways that help to protect their health.

Expectation

1

Students will demonstrate ways in which they can enhance and maintain their health and well-being.

Grade-level concepts and content	**Examples of skills and behaviors**

The human body:

Children at this level are curious about the function of body parts and their own bodies. Teaching them how their bodies function and the care required to maintain health empowers them to choose healthy behaviors. The curriculum should focus on habits related to physical care of the body and those related to protecting the body.

- Practicing good personal hygiene, including caring for teeth, gums, eyes, ears, nose, skin, hair, and nails
- Using protective equipment or practicing behaviors to protect the body, such as:
  1. Using a seat belt or helmet
  2. Using sunscreen or a hat in bright sunlight
  3. Keeping sharp objects away from one's eyes, ears, nose
  4. Protecting ears from exposure to excessive noise
  5. Wearing appropriate clothing and protective equipment for sports
  6. Playing or exercising at times and in ways that minimize exposure to such environmental hazards as excessive heat and smog

Students should understand how and be able to brush and floss their teeth.

57

Grade-level concepts and content	Examples of skills and behaviors

Food choices:

Because food preferences and dietary practices begin to be formed in childhood, students should begin investigating healthy eating patterns, exploring different food grouping systems, and learning how to select a variety of foods that promote health. They should become acquainted with the variety of foods available, including foods from various cultures, and have opportunities to try foods that may not be a part of their regular diet. The concept that all foods have a place in a healthy diet should be emphasized. Although some foods provide more of the things the body needs than other foods, none have to be eliminated from a healthy diet except for medical or religious reasons. The *California Daily Food Guide* and the USDA food pyramid should be introduced and used to assist students in making healthy food choices.

- Making healthy food choices
- Grouping foods in many different ways—for example, by taste, smell, feel, color, sound, origin (plant or animal), or category
- Establishing and maintaining healthy eating practices
- Preparing and trying a variety of healthy foods, using safe and sanitary food preparation and storage techniques
- Analyzing how food choices are influenced by peers, the media, the family, and the community

Physical activity:

Students should have opportunities to participate in enjoyable physical activities. As they enjoy movement, they can begin to develop an understanding of the means of achieving physical fitness. This

- Participating regularly in active play and a variety of enjoyable physical activities, with a focus on the pleasure of being active
- Obtaining a sufficient amount of sleep

Making healthy food choices means frequently eating fruit, vegetables, whole grains, and beans and selecting low-fat meats, fish, and poultry. It also means minimizing consumption of foods of low nutritional value.

Grade-level concepts and content	**Examples of skills and behaviors**
understanding includes knowing the characteristics of a physically fit person and the physical, mental, emotional, and social benefits of regular physical activity.	• Observing safety rules during physical activities • Exploring ways to engage in enjoyable out-of-school play activities that promote fitness and health

Mental and emotional health:

As children explore the effects that eating nutritious foods and exercising sufficiently have on good health, they should learn that good health is a dynamic, unified state of physical, mental, emotional, and social well-being. A balanced routine of rest, work, play, and healthy food choices contributes to physical fitness and good health. In addition, fostering good family relationships and friendships and learning to base one's actions on personal values and ethical considerations promote mental and emotional health. The curriculum should, therefore, help students learn to balance self-interest with concern and caring for others.	• Identifying and sharing feelings in appropriate ways • Demonstrating personal characteristics that contribute to self-confidence and self-esteem, such as honesty, integrity, respect for the dignity of others • Developing protective factors that help foster resiliency, such as participating in activities that promote positive bonding to peers and adults in the school and community and identifying a support system • Developing and using effective communication skills to enhance social interactions • Developing and using effective coping strategies, including critical thinking; effective decision making; goal setting; practice of problem-solving, assertiveness, and refusal skills; and taking time for exercise and relaxation • Avoiding self-destructive behaviors and practicing self-control

Expectation

2

Students will demonstrate behaviors that prevent disease and speed recovery from illness.

Grade-level concepts and content	*Examples of skills and behaviors*

Disease prevention:

In the early elementary years, children are encouraged to share such things as toys, supplies, and friendship with their classmates. They also need to learn what **not** to share; each person should use only his or her own toothbrush, cup, and comb.

The curriculum should emphasize how behaviors can help prevent disease or reduce its influence. Students can explore ways in which communicable diseases are spread by pathogens. They should begin to understand that the risk of developing chronic diseases is influenced not only by one's behavior but also by environmental conditions and genetic predisposition. The content should include symptoms of major communicable diseases and the effect immunizations, health screenings, and sanitary practices can have on preventing the spread of diseases. Students can also investigate how faulty handling, storage, and preparation of food can produce food-borne illnesses.

- Practicing good personal hygiene to prevent the spread of disease, such as washing one's hands and covering one's mouth when sneezing or coughing

- Practicing positive health behaviors to reduce the risk of disease, such as:

  1. Participating regularly in physical activities

  2. Making healthy food choices

  3. Acknowledging the importance of immunizations and demonstrating a willingness to cooperate in immunizations

  4. Limiting exposure to communicable diseases as much as possible

  5. Caring for wounds in a manner that supports healing

- Cooperating in regular health screenings, including dental examinations

60

Grade-level concepts and content	Examples of skills and behaviors

• Preparing food in the classroom or school cafeteria as a way of learning about the importance of sanitary food preparation and storage to avoid communicable diseases and food-borne illnesses

Treatment of disease:

Students at this level should investigate the common symptoms of illness and recognize that being responsible for personal health also means alerting parents, guardians, or appropriate health-care personnel to any symptoms of disease. Students should explore how their behavior can help them recover from disease or manage its effects over the long term. Why medicines should be taken properly and why they should be taken only under the supervision of responsible adults should be emphasized.

• Recognizing symptoms of common illnesses, such as fever, rashes, coughs, congestion, and wheezing and describing them to parents or health-care providers

• Cooperating with parents and health-care providers in the treatment or management of disease, such as asthma

• Taking prescription or over-the-counter medicines properly under the direction of parents or health-care providers

Expectation

3

Students will practice behaviors that reduce the risk of becoming involved in potentially dangerous situations and react to potentially dangerous situations in ways that help to protect their health.

Grade-level concepts and content	Examples of skills and behaviors

Potentially dangerous situations:

A key concept at this level is recognizing the potential for danger in everyday situations and behaving in ways that help to protect one's own safety and well-being. Students should be able to describe the characteristics of a safe environment and should be given opportunities to practice behaviors that promote a safe environment for themselves and others. The curriculum should include descriptions of potential dangers when students are in or near motor vehicles and when they are engaged in recreational activities, including references to drowning and falls. Students should know what to do if they become lost or separated from parents and should understand that they should never willingly go off with a stranger. They should be aware that being home alone is a big responsibility and is potentially dangerous. In addition, the curriculum should emphasize that young children should not handle firearms, which present a serious threat to the children's safety.

- Developing and using appropriate skills to identify, avoid when possible, and cope with potentially dangerous situations
- Practicing safe behavior in or near motorized vehicles, including crossing streets safely
- Practicing safe behavior in recreational activities, such as cycling and skating
- Practicing safe behavior in and near water
- Interacting safely with strangers
- Developing and using appropriate skills to avoid, resolve, and cope with conflicts
- Reporting or obtaining assistance when faced with unsafe situations
- Practicing behaviors that help prevent poisonings, including learning never to smell, taste, or swallow unfamiliar items

| *Grade-level concepts and content* | *Examples of skills and behaviors* |

Alcohol, tobacco, and other drugs:

Students should learn about the negative impact that chemical substances can have on health. The curriculum should discuss what drugs are, including alcohol, tobacco, and others, and describe the differences between helpful and potentially harmful substances. The concept of dependency should be introduced. And students should begin to learn to cope with an environment in which alcohol, tobacco, and other drugs are used and dependency exists by developing skills and behaviors that support positive health behaviors.

- Exercising self-control
- Developing and using interpersonal and other communication skills
- Distinguishing between helpful and harmful substances
- Identifying ways to cope with or seek assistance as necessary when confronted with situations involving alcohol, tobacco, and other drugs

Child abuse, including sexual exploitation:

After parents are notified and local standards are complied with, age-appropriate information about child abuse or neglect can be introduced. Included should be reference to each person's right to the privacy of his or her body and the appropriateness of telling others when touching is not welcome. Instruction should emphasize that a child is not at fault if the child is touched in an improper or uncomfortable way by an adult. The child's responsibility in this situation is to tell a trusted adult what had occurred.

- Identifying ways to seek assistance if worried, abused, or threatened, including how to tell a trusted adult if uncomfortable touching occurs
- Developing and using communication skills to tell others when touching is unwanted

63

Grade-level concepts and content	**Examples of skills and behaviors**

Emergencies:

Students should be taught appropriate ways to react during and after an emergency, including emergencies resulting from natural disasters, such as earthquakes. The first step is to recognize the seriousness of the situation. The second is to obtain assistance. Mitigating steps can substantially reduce health hazards resulting from natural disasters. Instruction should include descriptions of appropriate responses to fires and earthquakes and, depending on local needs, responses to such other potential disasters as floods.

The role of adults in emergencies should be emphasized. For example, parents or teachers can help children. However, if they are not available, children should know how to seek help from other appropriate adults.

- Recognizing emergencies and responding appropriately, including:
  1. Knowing how to get out of the home in the event of a fire
  2. Using a telephone appropriately to obtain help, including dialing 911 if available
  3. Providing name, address, and telephone number to a responsible adult
  4. Knowing how to treat simple injuries, such as scratches, cuts, bruises, and first-degree burns
  5. Practicing the stop, drop, and roll response to a clothing fire
  6. Identifying and obtaining help from police officers, fire fighters, and medical personnel
- Practicing appropriate behavior during fire drills, earthquake drills, and other disaster drills

Unifying Idea:
Respect for and
promotion of the
health of others

1. Students will play a positive, active role in promoting the health of their families.

2. Students will promote positive health practices within the school and community, including developing positive relationships with their peers.

Expectation

1

Students will play a positive, active role in promoting the health of their families.

Grade-level concepts and content	Examples of skills and behaviors

Roles of family members:

Students should learn that a common trait of all successful families is a commitment to fostering the physical, mental, emotional, and social welfare of every member. Healthy individuals are actively and positively involved with their families.

Students should explore the role of parents and the extended family in supporting a strong family and promoting the health of children. For example, the limits parents set for children, the values or religious beliefs taught, and the behaviors and values modeled

- Supporting and valuing all family members

- Demonstrating ways in which children can help support positive family interactions, such as listening to and following directions, following family rules, showing care and concern toward other family members, and interacting appropriately with family members

- Developing and using effective communication skills, including nonviolent conflict resolution

Grade-level concepts and content	*Examples of skills and behaviors*
influence the behavior of children. Students can also explore the role of health-related rules in promoting the health of family members. For example, parents may require children to stay home when they have certain illnesses.	
Students should explore the role of children in promoting the health of the family and begin to develop the skills necessary to be a supportive family member.	

Change and the family:

Such changes as pregnancy, birth, marriage, divorce or separation, illness, or death affect all family members and can generate strong emotions. Students should explore strategies for coping with change in the family.	• Identifying feelings related to changes within the family and effectively expressing them to others in a positive way • Using effective strategies to cope with change in the family, such as learning how to handle emotions by talking with a parent or other trusted adult about those feelings

Expectation

2

Students will promote positive health practices within the school and community, including developing positive relationships with their peers.

Grade-level concepts and content	*Examples of skills and behaviors*

Friendship and peer relationships:

The curriculum should include an opportunity for students to examine how positive peer relationships contribute to good health. This exploration will help to lay the foundation for resisting negative peer pressure in later years. Students should explore the importance of having friends and the characteristics of good friends and begin to examine how others influence their behavior. They should also be helped to recognize that good communication is important for developing and maintaining friendships and should be guided to seek out healthy, positive friendships.

Students should also be encouraged to respect the dignity and worth of others, all of whom have special talents and abilities. Positive interactions are different from friendships, however. Although we may not like everyone with

- Knowing and using appropriate ways to make new friends

- Demonstrating acceptable methods of gaining attention

- Demonstrating acceptable ways to show or express feelings

- Demonstrating positive actions toward others, including acts of trust, kindness, respect, affection, listening, patience, and forgiveness and avoiding demeaning statements directed toward others

- Resolving conflicts in a positive, constructive way

Grade-level concepts and content	**Examples of skills and behaviors**

whom we interact, being able to communicate and work effectively with a variety of individuals is an important skill.

Violence is a public health issue. When conflicts cannot be resolved in a nonviolent manner, society suffers. Recognizing that there are positive ways to resolve conflict, students should begin to develop conflict-resolution skills at this time. They should learn a variety of strategies for handling negative feelings, including feelings of anger and disappointment.

School and community-based efforts to promote and protect health:

Students should understand why rules about health exist at home and at school and why students should respect those rules and encourage their friends and family members to do so as well. Students should be encouraged to assume responsibility for following the rules without being specifically reminded. In addition, the curriculum should include opportunities for students to develop an understanding of the way behavior effects the environment and participate in school or community efforts to support positive health behaviors. For example, students might examine sources of litter and determine ways to lessen the problem.

- Understanding and following school rules related to health

- Participating in school efforts to promote health—for example, a walk-a-thon, fundraising events, or practices that support healthy food choices

- Assuming responsibility for helping to take care of the school, such as picking up trash on the school grounds or helping other students assume responsibility for that action

- Participating in community efforts to address local health and environmental issues—for example, recycling

Unifying Idea:
An understanding of the process of growth and development

Expectations:

1. Students will understand the variety of physical, mental, emotional, and social changes that occur throughout life.

2. Students will understand and accept individual differences in growth and development.

Expectation

1

Students will understand the variety of physical, mental, emotional, and social changes that occur throughout life.

Grade-level concepts and content	Examples of skills and behaviors

Life cycle:

Students should learn that all living things come from other living things and have life cycles. For humans this process includes physical, mental, emotional, and social growth. Students should understand the stages of the life cycle from infancy to old age.

- Describing the cycle of growth and development in humans and other animal species

- Demonstrating an understanding of the aging process, such as understanding why some older adults, including grandparents and great-grandparents, may have needs different from those of younger adults and children.

Expectation

2

Students will understand and accept individual differences in growth and development.

Grade-level concepts and content	**Examples of skills and behaviors**

Growth and development:

Students should explore the universal aspects of growth. However, they should also recognize that each individual has a unique pattern of growth and development. The major factors that determine individual differences, especially in height and weight, should be highlighted, including genetics and dietary and exercise habits.

Although persons with disabilities are different from others, they are not inferior. Students should be encouraged accept those with disabilities. They should try to walk in the shoes of a person with special needs and determine how they would like people to treat them if they had disabilities.

- Demonstrating an understanding of individual differences, such as differences in appearance or learning styles, through positive, constructive actions
- Adapting group activities to include a variety of individuals—for example, blind students or students in wheelchairs

Mental and emotional development:

Learning to name and recognize different emotions is a first step in learning to cope effectively with unpleasant feelings.

Students should explore the mental and emotional aspects of growth and development. For example, they should learn that many of the emotions they experience throughout life are

- Identifying, expressing, and managing feelings appropriately
- Developing and using effective communication skills

Grade-level concepts and content	Examples of skills and behaviors

also felt by other people. When feeling sad, angry, or confused, they will find that talking about feelings with a parent, trusted peer, or other adult is an appropriate coping skill.

Expectation:

Students will identify information, products, and services that may be helpful or harmful to their health.

Grade-level concepts and content	Examples of skills and behaviors

Products and services:

Students should begin to explore how the health-care system functions by identifying places for obtaining health services and learning what specific services are offered. They should identify types of health-care workers and individuals qualified to provide health advice and care, thereby laying the groundwork for a discussion of health quackery in later years. They should also explore sources of health-related information and products. Students at this grade span should begin to recognize that they are consumers and that consumer decisions are influenced by a variety of factors. They should begin to

- Identifying places for obtaining health and social services and learning what types of services are provided
- Identifying health-care workers
- Identifying a variety of consumer influences and analyzing how those influences affect decisions

Unifying Idea: *Informed use of health-related information, products, and services*

Grade-level concepts and content	*Examples of skills and behaviors*
explore the advertising strategies used to influence the selection and use of health-related products and services as well as the use of alcohol and tobacco.	

Food choices:

Students should explore how family, school, friends, the community, advertising, and the food industry all play a role in influencing what children prefer to eat, what is available for them to eat, and what their eating environments are like. Students should recognize that all of these factors influence the food choices they make.

Students should explore sources of nutrition information and recognize that food labels are a convenient and important source for this information. They should learn how to identify the contents of packaged foods and begin to learn how to use labels to compare food products. | • Reading and interpreting some of the information available on food labels, such as identifying sugar, salt, and fat as ingredients

• Using labels to compare the contents of food products

• Identifying ads and recognizing strategies used to influence decisions

• Practicing various positive responses to those influences |

Grades Three Through Six

Students in grades three through six are assuming more responsibility for their own health and well-being. They can benefit from instruction that fosters the development of positive health behaviors and prevention of negative, unhealthy behaviors. Particularly important in the middle grades is the onset of adolescence, which can begin as early as third grade for some students. Others will develop more slowly. Students at this level begin to become acutely aware of their physical development and the varying rates of development among their peers. In addition, children's orientation to the peer group tends to increase during this age span. Most children experience a growing need to be and feel normal at precisely the time when growth and development vary widely even within the same classroom. Many students are also likely to feel pressure to act grown-up by experimenting with alcohol, tobacco, or other drugs. Acceptance of differences in individual growth and development as well as strategies to prevent the use of alcohol, tobacco, and other drugs need to be woven throughout the curriculum at this time.

Expectations:

1. Students will demonstrate ways in which they can enhance and maintain their own health and well-being.

2. Students will demonstrate behaviors that prevent disease and speed recovery from illness.

3. Students will practice behaviors that reduce the risk of becoming involved in potentially dangerous situations and react to those situations in ways that help to protect their health.

Unifying Idea:
Acceptance of personal responsibility for lifelong health

Expectation

1

Students will demonstrate ways in which they can enhance and maintain their own health and well-being.

Grade-level concepts and content	Examples of skills and behaviors

The human body:

As students assume responsibility for personal care and self-grooming, they should continue to explore the link between their behavior and health. For example, as puberty begins, behavioral changes related to personal health habits may be involved for some students.

The curriculum at this level should also include more in-depth information about body systems and their relation to personal health. Students should learn how body systems are interrelated, how they function to fight disease, and how they are influenced by environmental conditions.

- Practicing good personal hygiene, with particular attention to the changing needs of preadolescents and adolescents

- Using protective equipment, such as a helmet when cycling, or practicing behaviors to protect the body, such as applying sunscreen when appropriate

Food choices:

Building on the concepts and skills learned at the kindergarten through grade three level, students should continue to explore how food choices can

- Making healthy food choices, with emphasis on:

■ Identifies previously introduced skills or behaviors that should be built on and reinforced.

More attention to personal care helps maintain healthy skin.

Grade-level concepts and content	Examples of skills and behaviors
affect their health and well-being. They should continue to learn about food classification systems and begin to learn about the nutrients in foods. *The California Daily Food Guide* and the USDA food pyramid should be used to assist students in making healthy food choices from a variety of ethnic cuisines. The effects food choices have on body composition and optimal health should be explored as well as the dangers of eating disorders. Students should examine how food-preparation methods and food-handling practices affect the safety and nutrient quality of foods.	1. Basing decisions upon nutrient content 2. Selecting foods that promote oral health ■ Establishing and maintaining healthy eating practices ■ Preparing a variety of healthy foods, using safe and sanitary food preparation and storage techniques, with an emphasis on how food-handling and preparation practices affect the safety and nutrient quality of foods ■ Analyzing how food choices are influenced • Practicing kitchen safety, such as using knives, stoves, and ovens correctly and carefully

The relationship between food choices and eating habits and dental decay can be explored as students learn more about nutrition.

Physical activity:

Students should continue to enjoy physical activities and should learn to set and use personal goals for developing or maintaining physical fitness, recognizing that even moderate regular activity can help prevent obesity and heart disease. Students should also investigate the relationships involving aerobic endurance, body composition, flexibility, muscular strength and endurance, and self-image.	■ Obtaining a sufficient amount of sleep ■ Observing safety rules during physical activities ■ Exploring ways to engage in enjoyable out-of-school play activities that promote fitness and health • Participating regularly in a variety of enjoyable physical activities that promote aerobic conditioning, flexibility, and muscular strength and endurance both inside and outside of school • Setting personal fitness goals

As they enter puberty, students should develop appropriate strategies for coping with the emotional turmoil of adolescence.

Grade-level concepts and content	Examples of skills and behaviors

Mental and emotional development:

Mental and emotional health, like physical fitness, can be cultivated and enhanced. Students in grades three through six have an increasing sensitivity to peer influence and feel acutely the need to belong to a group. The curriculum should continue to include opportunities for students to identify and seek protective factors that help foster resiliency. Students should learn that although preadolescence and adolescence are frequently periods of emotional turmoil, various coping strategies can be used to overcome feelings of inadequacy and depression.

High self-esteem and a sense of optimism and control over one's life are linked to one's success as a happy, productive human being. Students should have opportunities to bond to the school and community and to receive positive recognition for success. This age level is appropriate for introducing students to the effects of stress, including a discussion of what causes stress and how it can be detrimental to health unless various coping strategies are used to deal with it.

- Identifying and sharing feelings in appropriate ways
- Demonstrating personal characteristics that contribute to self-confidence and self-esteem, such as honesty, integrity, respect for the dignity of others
- Developing protective factors that help foster resiliency, such as participating in activities that promote positive bonding to peers, and adults in the school and the community
- Developing and using effective communication skills
- Developing and using effective coping strategies, including critical thinking, effective decision making, goal setting, and problem solving; practicing assertiveness and refusal skills; and taking time for exercise and relaxation
- Avoiding self-destructive behaviors
- Practicing strategies for resisting negative peer pressure

Expectation

2

Students will demonstrate behaviors that prevent disease and speed recovery from illness.

Grade-level concepts and content	Examples of skills and behaviors

Disease prevention:

A wide range of communicable and chronic diseases, including genetic disorders, should be the focus of the curriculum for this outcome at this grade span. Students should develop an understanding of the difference between communicable and noncommunicable diseases. Causes of diseases and the role of positive health practices (e.g., regular medical and dental examinations, immunizations, aerobic exercise, proper nutrition) in avoiding, delaying, or minimizing the onset of diseases should also be emphasized. The curriculum should investigate how people with diseases are treated, including how prejudice and ignorance can lead to discrimination against persons with diseases or chronic conditions.

■ Practicing good personal hygiene to prevent the spread of disease

■ Practicing positive health behaviors to reduce the risk of disease

■ Cooperating in regular health screenings, including dental examinations

• Demonstrating safely care and concern toward ill persons in the family, the school, and the community

■ Identifies previously introduced skills or behaviors that should be built on and reinforced.

Grade-level concepts and content	Examples of skills and behaviors

Treatment of disease:

As students take more responsibility for their health, they develop a deeper understanding of the need to follow prescribed health-care procedures and cooperate with parents and health-care providers to facilitate recovery from disease when possible or to enhance long-term management of chronic diseases. The treatment or management of the major communicable and chronic diseases should be presented, including scientific contributions that have helped to protect people from disease and disorders. Students who have health problems or chronic conditions should begin to accept responsibility for their role in treatment, including the proper use of medication. The effects of family and cultural influences on the care of disease and the usefulness of participating in support groups or activities should also be explored.

- Recognizing symptoms of common illnesses

- Cooperating in treatment or management of disease, with an emphasis on accepting responsibility for such cooperation and communicating appropriately with parents and health-care providers

- Taking prescription and over-the-counter medicines properly; never taking medicine prescribed for someone else

- Interpreting correctly instructions for taking medicine

Expectation

3

Students will practice behaviors that reduce the risk of becoming involved in potentially dangerous situations and react to potentially dangerous situations in ways that help to protect their health.

Grade-level concepts and content	*Examples of skills and behaviors*

Potentially dangerous situations:

At this level students should learn that some potentially dangerous situations can be handled through routine safety precautions, including behaving appropriately in or near motor vehicles; observing safe play and exercise practices; identifying hazards in the home, school, and community; and participating in activities to remove hazards.

Students should understand how to minimize the potential for injury when interacting with others who exhibit dangerous behavior. For example, one option is to leave the situation or, if appropriate, encourage the individual to stop the dangerous behavior. Conflict-resolution skills should be further refined and practiced.

■ Developing and using appropriate skills to identify, avoid when possible, and cope with potentially dangerous situations

■ Practicing safe behavior in and near motorized vehicles

■ Practicing safe behavior in recreational activities

■ Practicing safe behavior in and near water

■ Developing and using appropriate skills to avoid, resolve, and cope with conflicts, emphasizing how peers can help each other avoid and cope with conflict

• Understanding and following rules prohibiting possession of weapons at school

■ Reporting or obtaining assistance when faced with unsafe situations

■ Identifies previously introduced skills or behaviors that should be built on and reinforced.

Nonviolent conflict-resolution skills, anger management, and good communication skills can all help to prevent violence.

Grade-level concepts and content	Examples of skills and behaviors
	Alcohol, tobacco, and other drugs:

Students should make a commitment not to use or distribute alcohol, tobacco, or other drugs. They should be given opportunities to develop the skills needed to keep that commitment.

Because experimentation with alcohol, tobacco, or other drugs often begins in the upper elementary grades, students should develop the knowledge, skills, and strategies for choosing not to use a wide range of harmful chemical substances. They should learn ways to identify drugs; the effects of drugs on different parts of the body; the reasons for not using specific substances; and the effects and consequences of use. In addition, they should learn the school rules prohibiting the use of alcohol, tobacco, and other drugs and should be aware that these substances are illegal for minors or all persons. Students should understand the influences that promote drug use and develop the skills necessary to resist those influences; know how and where to obtain help when confronted with potentially dangerous or harmful situations involving chemical substances; and make a commitment not to use or distribute alcohol, tobacco, or other drugs.

- Exercising self-control
- Developing and using interpersonal and other communication skills, such as assertiveness, refusal, negotiation, and conflict-resolution skills, to avoid use of alcohol, tobacco, and other drugs
- Distinguishing between helpful and harmful substances
- Identifying ways to cope with or seek assistance as necessary when confronted with situations involving alcohol, tobacco, or other drugs
- Differentiating between the use and misuse of prescription and nonprescription drugs
- Avoiding, recognizing, and responding to negative social influences and pressure to use alcohol, tobacco, or other drugs
- Using positive peer pressure to help counteract the negative effects of living in an environment where alcohol, tobacco, or other drug abuse or dependency exists
- Identifying ways of obtaining help to resist pressure to use alcohol, tobacco, or other drugs

Grade-level concepts and content	Examples of skills and behaviors

Child abuse, including sexual exploitation:

Students should be aware that no one, not even a parent, has the right to abuse a child or another family member physically. Neglect and child abuse are serious problems that may require outside assistance.

After parents are notified, the strategies presented in discussions of alcohol, tobacco, and other drugs can be expanded to help students learn how to resist pressure to become sexually active and where to seek help or advice if needed. Information on how to resist sexual abuse or exploitation should also be presented.

- Identifying ways to seek assistance if concerned, abused, or threatened, including how to overcome fear of telling

- Recognizing and avoiding situations that can increase risk of abuse, such as leaning into a car when giving directions to a stranger

Emergencies:

Building on earlier instruction in proper responses to natural disasters, students should have the opportunity to learn and demonstrate emergency preparation procedures and proficiency in basic first-aid procedures, including proper response to breathing and choking problems, bleeding, shock, poisonings, and minor burns. Older students can also learn cardiopulmonary resuscitation, in addition to basic first aid, if taught by certified instructors.

- Recognizing emergencies and responding appropriately, including:

  1. Knowing where to find emergency supplies, such as a flashlight and a first-aid kit

  2. Demonstrating proficiency in basic first-aid procedures, such as proper response to breathing and choking problems, bleeding, shock, poisonings, and minor burns

  3. Using universal precautions when dealing with other people's blood

The term *universal precautions* refers to a method of infection control in which all human blood and other potentially infectious materials are treated as if known to be infected with HIV or hepatitis B. Universal precautions include using latex gloves when aiding an injured person, washing hands with soap and water, using disinfectants, and disposing of trash properly.

Grade-level concepts and content	*Examples of skills and behaviors*
	• Understanding the family emergency plan and developing the skills necessary to follow the plan

Unifying Idea: *Respect for and promotion of the health of others*

Expectations:

1. Students will play a positive, active role in promoting the health of their families.

2. Students will promote positive health practices within the school and community, including developing positive relationships with their peers.

Expectation

1

Students will play a positive, active role in promoting the health of their families.

Roles of family members:

Building on the concept of the family as a major source of an individual's health, students should recognize that because the roles of children change as they mature, parents may have different expectations of children versus adolescents. Students should explore ways in which they can contribute to their family, including participating in family activities, practicing health-promoting behaviors with the family, and

■ Supporting and valuing all family members

■ Demonstrating ways in which children can help support positive family interactions

■ Developing and using effective communication skills

• Practicing health-promoting behaviors with the family, such as encouraging family

_____

■ Identifies previously introduced skills or behaviors that should be built on and reinforced.

82

Grade-level concepts and content	*Examples of skills and behaviors*
assuming more responsibility for household tasks.	walks and meals at which the entire family is present • Participating in daily activities that help maintain the family

Change and the family:

Changes within and outside the family may affect both individuals and family members. Students at this grade level should have the opportunity to examine the effects of change on the family and develop coping strategies to deal with changes when they occur. The important point to consider is that although families are challenged by such events as a serious illness or divorce, families can and do cope and may in fact grow stronger as a result of the challenge. Good communication in a family is a key coping skill, and positive ways to resolve conflict should continue to be addressed. Students should be able to identify community resources that provide help to families with problems.	■ Identifying feelings related to changes within the family and effectively expressing them to others in a positive way ■ Using effective strategies to cope with change in the family, including identifying a support system

Expectation

2

Students will promote positive health practices within the school and community, including positive relationships with peers.

Grade-level concepts and content	*Examples of skills and behaviors*

Friendship and peer relationships:

Students should explore how individuals can play active roles in promoting healthy relationships with peers. They should be aware that peer influence has the potential to be either positive or negative. Students should be encouraged to seek opportunities to be a positive role model.

- Knowing and using appropriate ways to make new friends
- Demonstrating acceptable methods of gaining attention
- Demonstrating acceptable ways to show or express feelings
- Demonstrating positive actions toward others
- Resolving conflicts in a positive, constructive way
- Demonstrating how to resist negative peer pressure

School and community-based efforts to promote and protect health:

Students should explore how their school promotes and protects the health of students. For example, students should examine school policies related to health, nutrition, and safety and understand the reasons for those policies. They should understand that by following the policies, they are helping to

- Understanding and following school rules related to health
- Participating in school efforts to promote health; for example, helping to select fundraising activities that are consistent with efforts to

---

■ Identifies previously introduced skills or behaviors that should be built on and reinforced.

Students should recognize the power of positive peer role models and be encouraged to be a good influence on their friends.

Grade-level concepts and content

promote health at school. Further, students should explore how individuals can play active roles in the school and community to promote health and should have opportunities to participate in positive health practices in school and community settings.

They should begin to explore the role of the health department and other community health and social service agencies in health promotion and disease prevention. Local, state, and national laws and regulations that promote public health and the safety of the community should be identified and examined, including those designed to protect the environment. Recycling, developing safe and adequate food supplies and environmentally safe food packaging, and dealing with hunger and food waste within their communities should be introduced. Students should investigate ways in which they can participate in or enhance school and community efforts to promote health.

Examples of skills and behaviors

promote health, such as choosing a jog-a-thon rather than a candy sale

■ Assuming responsibility for helping to take care of the school, such as picking up trash on the school grounds and helping other students assume responsibility for that action

■ Participating in community efforts to address local health and environmental issues

• Contributing to the strengthening of health-related policies at school, such as serving on a student safety committee

• Recognizing that public policies and laws influence health-related issues

Unifying Idea:
An understanding of the process of growth and development

Expectations:

1. Students will understand the variety of physical, mental, emotional, and social changes that occur throughout life.

2. Students will understand and accept individual differences in growth and development.

Expectation

1

Students will understand the variety of physical, mental, emotional, and social changes that occur throughout life.

Grade-level concepts and content	Examples of skills and behaviors

Life cycle:

Note: The *Education Code* requires parental notification before discussion of human reproductive organs and their functions and processes.

Students at this level are beginning to enter puberty and are curious, perhaps concerned, about the physical changes they are experiencing. Instruction should emphasize that all people are sexual beings and that it is natural for preadolescents and adolescents to want to understand human sexuality. The curriculum should help students understand the human reproductive process and the physical, mental, emotional,

- Recognizing the changes that occur during preadolescence

- Using correct terminology for body parts

- Practicing good personal hygiene, paying particular attention to the changing needs of preadolescents and adolescents

- Recognizing emotions

- Managing feelings appropriately, including being able to express feelings and practice self-control

- Developing and using effective communication skills to discuss with parents or other

Grade-level concepts and content

and social changes that occur during puberty. To be included are descriptions of sexual maturation, acne, changes in voice, growth of body and facial hair, menstruation, and sperm development. As they reach puberty, students should be made aware of toxic shock syndrome (TSS), its symptoms, and the means of preventing it. Also important are the social and emotional changes of adolescence—for example, a growing sensitivity to peer influence, family tensions, and mood swings. Cognitive and intellectual development should also be considered. Students should be encouraged to talk to their parents or other responsible adults if they have questions about sexuality or puberty and related changes.

Examples of skills and behaviors

trusted adults the changes that occur during preadolescence

Expectation

2

Students will understand and accept individual differences in growth and development.

Growth and development:

The rate of change during puberty varies with each individual. Students should be encouraged to be comfortable with their own progress and to like and accept themselves. The

- Demonstrating an understanding of individual differences

■ Identifies previously introduced skills or behaviors that should be built on and reinforced.

Students should understand differences in the rates of growth and development and be encouraged to include students with disabilities in group activities.

Grade-level concepts and content	Examples of skills and behaviors
curriculum should emphasize that there is no perfect body type and that people vary widely in size, height, shape, and rate of maturation.	■ Adapting group activities to include a variety of individuals • Developing a realistic body image • Recognizing problems associated with not having a realistic body image, including dieting and eating disorders, and seeking appropriate help

Mental and emotional development:

Students should continue to explore the mental and emotional aspects of growing and developing. They should be encouraged to focus on the future and develop strategies for coping with the changes of adolescence. Instruction should emphasize understanding differences, including individuals' unique strengths and weaknesses and the ways in which students can support each other in facing the uncertainties of adolescence. It is especially important at this time, when many students begin to be more group-oriented, to emphasize the need to include all students, especially those with disabilities and special needs.

■ Identifying, expressing, and managing feelings appropriately

■ Developing and using effective communication skills

• Recognizing one's own strengths and limitations

• Developing and using coping strategies, including critical thinking, effective decision making, goal setting, and problem solving; developing assertiveness and refusal skills; and taking time for exercise and relaxation

• Developing a focus on the future, such as having realistic short-term and long-term goals and delaying gratification

Expectation:		**Unifying Idea:**

Students will identify information, products, and services that may be helpful or harmful to their health.

Unifying Idea: *Informed use of health-related information, products, and services*

Grade-level concepts and content	Examples of skills and behaviors

Products and services:

Students at this level should begin to identify the range of health services in the community and explore how their families can access needed services, including developing the ability to distinguish between situations that require health services and those that do not. An examination of community health services can be linked to an exploration of health-related careers, including careers related to food preparation and food service.

Consumer health care products are another important focus of the curriculum at this level. Students should be able to distinguish products and services that are necessary, those that are not necessary, and those that may be harmful. Characteristics of health care quackery should be presented. To be included is the idea that quackery is more likely to flourish in those areas of health—pain management,

■ Identifying places for obtaining health services and social services and knowing what types of services are provided

■ Identifying health-care workers

■ Identifying a variety of consumer influences and analyzing how those influences affect decisions

• Recognizing helpful products and services

• Using critical-thinking skills to analyze marketing and advertising techniques and their influence on the selection of health-related services and products

• Seeking care from the school nurse or school-linked services together with their families when appropriate, such as when needed for proper management of asthma

---

■ Identifies previously introduced skills or behaviors that should be built on and reinforced.

Grade-level concepts and content	Examples of skills and behaviors
beauty aids, weight control, cancer treatment—where standard medicine is least successful or when expectations are unrealistic. Students should look critically at health claims and the factors that influence the selection of products and services, including ways in which advertising and peer pressure can influence students' images of themselves.	• Discussing home care with parents when appropriate

Food choices:

Looking critically at health claims and food advertisements helps students become thoughtful consumers.

As students mature, they become increasingly more responsible for their own health and have greater opportunities to purchase and prepare their own food. Thus, the need for good consumer skills increases. Students should explore the influence of self-image, peer influences, and advertising on food choices. They should learn to use all the information on food labels when making decisions about which foods to buy and should have opportunities to learn basic food-preparation and handling techniques.

Because of their growing independence, many students have more frequent opportunities to eat away from home. As a result they have opportunities to try new foods and practice ways to maintain a nutritionally balanced diet. The

- ■ Reading and interpreting the information available on food labels, such as the amount of sugar, salt, or fat contained in the food
- ■ Using labels to compare the contents of food products, including a comparison of the cost of various foods according to their nutritional value
- • Using critical-thinking skills to analyze marketing and advertising techniques and their influence on food selection
- • Using valid nutrition information to make healthy food choices
- • Purchasing nutritious foods in a variety of settings

Grade-level concepts and content

curriculum should include ways to make food choices in a variety of eating environments, including fast-food outlets. As their circle of friends expands, students will have greater exposure to differing family customs, backgrounds, and eating patterns. This is an opportune time to explore a variety of ethnic and cultural foods, food patterns, and customs, using both the classroom and the school cafeteria.

Examples of skills and behaviors

- Using unit pricing to determine the most economical purchases
- Analyzing and tasting foods from different ethnic and cultural groups
- Developing basic food-preparation skills, including safe and sanitary food preparation and storage

Grades Six Through Nine

Students in grades six through nine are becoming more independent of their parents and increasingly more subject to peer approval than are younger children. They are concerned, at times preoccupied, with changes in their bodies and they often begin to focus on themselves and to be critical of themselves and others. Able to understand that certain behaviors have undesirable consequences, they may have difficulty in accepting that such consequences could happen to them. An awareness of immediate consequences (for example, bad breath as a result of smoking) rather than long-term consequences is more likely to motivate students. The curriculum for this grade span focuses in part on the personal health habits appropriate to the changing needs of adolescents. But students should also continue to explore and practice the skills necessary for developing lifelong positive health habits. Although prevention remains the mainstay of the curriculum at this level, additional elements are the early identification of health problems and appropriate intervention. Students should always be encouraged to discuss personal and health problems with their parents or guardians. Information about local resources for health-related support and assistance should also be provided as part of the curriculum.

Unifying Idea:
Acceptance of personal responsibility for lifelong health

Expectations:

1. Students will demonstrate ways in which they can enhance and maintain their own health and well-being.

2. Students will demonstrate behaviors that prevent disease and speed recovery from illness.

3. Students will practice behaviors that reduce the risk of becoming involved in potentially dangerous situations and react to potentially dangerous situations in ways that help to protect their health.

Expectation

1

Students will demonstrate ways in which they can enhance and maintain their own health and well-being.

Grade-level concepts and content	Examples of skills and behaviors

The human body:

The immediate and long-term effects of personal health habits on body systems are appropriate areas of study for this grade span. For example, students might explore the short-term and long-term effects of a high-fat diet and a sedentary life-style on the cardiovascular system. They should continue to examine how body systems are interconnected and how the immune system prevents or combats disease. Because environmental conditions also affect body systems, students should be able to demonstrate ways to protect themselves from exposure to conditions that are potentially harmful.

■ Practicing good personal hygiene, including accepting responsibility for making those behaviors part of a normal routine

■ Recognizing and avoiding when possible, environmental conditions that are potentially harmful, such as exposure to pesticides or lead paint

■ Using protective equipment, such as goggles to protect the eyes when appropriate, or practicing behaviors to protect the body, such as applying sunscreen, exercising, or making healthy food choices

---

■ Identifies previously introduced skills or behaviors that should be built on and reinforced.

Grade-level concepts and content	**Examples of skills and behaviors**
As they continue to explore the unifying idea of acceptance of personal responsibility and the human body, students continue to recognize that a perfect body type does not exist and that people vary widely in size, height, shape, and rate of maturation. They should be encouraged to be comfortable with their own progress and to like and accept themselves.	• Recognizing and accepting differences in body types and maturation levels

Food choices:

Students should be encouraged to develop a personal nutrition plan based on food choices and calorie levels that promotes health and reduces the risk of disease. They should continue to explore the wide variety of healthy food choices available in all cultures and should have opportunities to taste and prepare low-cost foods and favorite foods in ways that make those foods healthy choices. The content should include the interrelationships among total calories, food sources of calories, energy expenditure, and body composition. Because adolescents have unique nutritional needs, they should understand that the variety and quantity of food they eat can influence their growth and development. Further, they should examine how their food choices are	■ Making healthy food choices in a variety of settings, including the selection of foods according to calculated energy expenditure and healthy body composition • Comparing caloric values of foods according to the percentage of fat, protein, and carbohydrate they contain ■ Establishing and maintaining healthy eating practices ■ Preparing a variety of healthy foods, using safe food preparation and storage techniques ■ Analyzing how food choices are influenced • Selecting appropriate practices to maintain, lose, or gain weight according to individual needs and scientific research

| **Grade-level concepts and content** | **Examples of skills and behaviors** |

influenced by their own emotions and by other sources, such as their peers or the media.

Physical activity:

Students should be made aware of the importance of variety and enjoyment in maintaining an exercise program and should have opportunities to participate regularly in a variety of physical activities at school and outside school. In addition, they should continue to set personal goals for developing or maintaining physical fitness. They should look for opportunities to set up a personal fitness program because a physically active life-style contributes to their personal health. They should examine the influence of frequency, intensity, duration, and type of physical activity on aerobic endurance, body composition, flexibility, and muscular strength and endurance. Finally, they should analyze ways in which physical activity contributes to physical, mental, emotional, and social health.

- Obtaining a sufficient amount of sleep
- Observing safety rules during physical activities
- Exploring ways to engage in out-of-school activities that promote fitness and health
- Participating regularly in a variety of enjoyable physical activities
- Developing and initiating a personal fitness plan that includes setting fitness goals and monitoring progress toward meeting those goals

Students should be encouraged to enjoy a variety of physical activities and seek safe ways to be physically active out of school.

Mental and emotional health:

Students' explorations of the mental and emotional aspects of health should build on those examined at earlier grade levels. Particular emphasis

- Demonstrating personal characteristics that contribute to self-confidence and self-esteem, such as honesty, integrity, responsibility, and

95

Although there is no such thing as a suicidal type, studies have shown that some adolescents exhibiting certain characteristics are at higher risk for suicide. These include students who have attempted suicide previously; students with little self-esteem; individuals who are severely depressed or who have been abused, neglected, or molested; teenagers in trouble; gay and lesbian students; perfectionists; learning-disabled students; loners; and abusers of alcohol or drugs. Often these students feel rejected or socially isolated.

—Suicide Prevention Program for California Public Schools

Grade-level concepts and content

should be placed on emotional development during adolescence, including an examination of mood swings, depression, and suicide. Students should understand that seeking assistance for mental and emotional problems is appropriate and should have opportunities to develop the skills needed to seek assistance. The positive aspects of mental and emotional health, such as friendship, continue to be of great importance and should also receive attention in the curriculum. In addition, students should continue to explore the connections between physical, mental, emotional, and social health and should be encouraged to pursue leisure-time activities that promote that health.

The curriculum should provide opportunities for all students to feel valued and have experiences that foster positive bonding to their peers, school, and community. These experiences are especially important for students at higher risk for suicide because these students thereby learn to cope with feelings of isolation, inadequacy, sadness, and depression and begin to overcome those feelings. Strategies that can be explored to help students cope with those feelings include talking over

Examples of skills and behaviors

respecting the dignity of others

■ Developing protective factors that help foster resiliency, such as participating in activities that promote positive bonding to peers and adults in the school and community, and developing and maintaining a focus on the future

■ Developing and using effective communication skills

■ Developing and using effective coping strategies, emphasizing strategies for coping with feelings of inadequacy, sadness, and depression. Examples include talking over problems with parents or religious leaders, understanding that feelings of isolation and depression will pass, examining the situation leading to the feelings, seeking appropriate assistance if depression persists, obtaining appropriate health care for depression, and participating in regular aerobic exercise

■ Avoiding self-destructive behaviors

■ Practicing strategies for resisting negative peer pressure

• Identifying the strongest risk factors for negative behaviors in their own lives and developing effective strategies for

Grade-level concepts and content	**Examples of skills and behaviors**

problems, understanding that feelings of isolation and depression will pass, examining the situation leading to the feelings, seeking appropriate assistance if depression persists, obtaining medical treatment for organically caused depression, and participating in regular aerobic exercise.

counteracting the effect of these risk factors

• Managing strong feelings and boredom

• Selecting entertainment that promotes mental and physical health

Expectation

2

Students will demonstrate behaviors that prevent disease and speed recovery from illness.

Disease prevention:

Students should acquire the knowledge and skills needed to develop a personal action plan for the prevention or early detection of disease.

Students should focus on the major chronic and communicable diseases prevalent at different stages of life, analyzing risks for contracting specific diseases based on pathogenic, genetic, environmental, and behavioral factors. They should continue to explore how positive health practices, such as aerobic exercise and proper nutrition, influence the risk and severity of disease. They should also learn how common behav-

■ Practicing good personal hygiene to prevent the spread of disease

■ Practicing positive health behaviors to reduce the risk of disease

■ Cooperating in regular health screenings, including dental examinations

■ Safely demonstrating care and concern toward ill persons in the family, the school, and the community

• Making a commitment to abstain from sexual activity

■ Identifies previously introduced skills or behaviors that should be built on and reinforced.

Grade-level concepts and content	*Examples of skills and behaviors*
ioral disorders contribute to chronic conditions, perhaps studying anorexia nervosa and its complications. They should begin to learn self-exam procedures and understand the role of self-examination in early detection of disease. In addition to learning how to prevent and cope with diseases in themselves, students should learn that people with diseases need the support and compassion of others.	• Practicing and using effective self-examination procedures

The prevention of sexually transmitted diseases (STDs), especially HIV/AIDS, should be emphasized at this grade span but only after consideration of *Education Code* mandates (see Appendix A). Students should be able to describe the causes of HIV infection and other sexually transmitted diseases as well as modes of transmission, symptoms, effects, and methods of prevention.

A strong emphasis should be placed on abstinence from sexual activity and safer sexual practices for those youths who are sexually active. However, sexual activity ("safe sex") is not being advocated. Abstinence from sexual activity is the only totally effective way to avoid unwanted pregnancy and sexually transmitted diseases and should be emphasized as the best choice for physical and emotional reasons.

Grade-level concepts and content	Examples of skills and behaviors

Treatment of disease:

Students at this level should be encouraged to take greater responsibility for the treatment of disease. They need to learn the symptoms of common diseases among youths and the importance of early diagnosis and treatment, including home treatment for common illnesses and the treatment and management of major diseases. In addition, they should learn when to seek qualified medical help. The curriculum should continue its focus on the importance of following prescribed health-care procedures and cooperating with parents and health-care providers to facilitate recovery or long-term treatment of diseases. Other topics appropriate for this grade span are the proper use of medication, including how to identify possible side effects, and personal rights and responsibilities involved in the treatment of disease. The influence of family and culture on the treatment of disease and the usefulness of participating in support groups or activities should continue to be explored.

■ Recognizing symptoms of common illnesses

■ Taking prescription and over-the-counter medicines properly

■ Interpreting correctly instructions written on medicine container labels, including using information provided with prescription and over-the-counter medicines to determine potential side effects

• Determining when treatment of illness at home is appropriate and when and how to seek further help when needed

• Accepting responsibility for active involvement in the treatment or management of disease, including practicing and using effective communication skills to discuss illness with parents and health-care providers

Although students should be encouraged to assume greater responsibility in treating illnesses, they should know that there are times when they need to seek adult assistance.

Expectation

3

Students will practice behaviors that reduce the risk of becoming involved in potentially dangerous situations and react to such situations in ways that help to protect their health.

Grade-level concepts and content	*Examples of skills and behaviors*

Potentially dangerous situations:

Because students in this age group may be especially prone to high-risk behavior, they should be given special instruction in ways to safeguard their lives. For example, they should be made familiar with the basic rules of traffic safety, including rules for drivers, occupants of motor vehicles, bicyclists, and pedestrians. And they should be taught to understand that traffic safety requires being observant at all times because others may not obey the rules.

Many potentially dangerous situations can be avoided or handled through the practice of safety precautions and the use of safety equipment in daily living. Students should learn to identify hazards found in the home, school, and community and participate in activities to remove those hazards.

Students should understand how to minimize the potential

- Developing and using appropriate skills to identify, avoid when possible, and cope with potentially dangerous situations, with emphasis on how peers can help each other avoid or cope with potentially dangerous situations in healthy ways

- Practicing safe behavior in and near motorized vehicles

- Practicing safe behavior in recreational activities, even in the absence of adults

- Practicing safe behavior in and near water

- Using appropriate skills to avoid, resolve, and cope with conflicts

- Understanding and following rules prohibiting possession of weapons at school

---

■ Identifies previously introduced skills or behaviors that should be built on and reinforced.

Students should learn to avoid unsafe activities even when pressured by peers to participate. They can refuse to take part in dares or hazing, diving into water of unknown depth, or activities that lack adequate adult supervision.

Grade-level concepts and content	Examples of skills and behaviors

for injury when interacting with others who exhibit dangerous behavior. Violence threatens the safety of individuals and society. Effective instruction in violence prevention should include opportunities to practice nonharmful conflict-resolution strategies, including identification of the variety of factors that can influence such resolution. Students should understand the importance of obeying school rules prohibiting the possession and use of weapons.

■ Reporting or obtaining assistance when faced with unsafe situations

• Identifying factors that reduce risks of accidents and demonstrating corrective action

• Identifying environmental factors that affect health and safety

• Recognizing that the use of alcohol and other drugs plays a role in many dangerous situations

• Demonstrating how peers can help each other avoid and cope with potentially dangerous situations in healthy ways

• Using thinking and decision-making skills in high-risk situations involving the use of motor vehicles and other hazardous activities

Alcohol, tobacco, and other drugs:

The use of alcohol, tobacco, or other drugs frequently plays a role in the dangerous behaviors of adolescents and adults. Students should understand the short-term and long-term effects of using such substances, including those that may alter performance, such as steroids. Their effects on the health of unborn children should also be explored. Students should develop their

■ Exercising self-control

■ Developing and using inter-personal and other communication skills, such as assertiveness, refusal, negotiation, and conflict-resolution skills to avoid the use of alcohol, tobacco, and other drugs

■ Distinguishing between helpful and harmful substances

101

Students should learn that they are not responsible for curing another's problems and that there are responsible adults and services that can provide help when needed.

Grade-level concepts and content

understanding of the concept of chemical dependency and the effects of such dependency on the body. Another concern should be the effects on society of the use of alcohol, tobacco, and other drugs. Students should learn what laws (local, state, and federal), school policies, and family rules govern the use of chemical substances and should understand the consequences of illegal use of drugs. They should also be taught to understand the influence of peers and the media on the use of alcohol, tobacco, and other drugs; develop knowledge, skills, and strategies for choosing not to use or distribute such substances; and learn strategies for avoiding drug-related risk-taking situations and should have opportunities to practice those strategies.

Numerous resources in the school and the community are available for people who have problems related to alcohol or drugs. However, many of the risk factors associated with the use of alcohol, tobacco, and other drugs are outside the student's control. A history of alcoholism at home, for example, or the easy availability of other drugs in the home or neighborhood are realities for many students. Even in adverse circumstances, however, stu-

Examples of skills and behaviors

- Differentiating between the use and misuse of prescription and nonprescription drugs
- Avoiding, recognizing, and responding to negative social influences and pressure to use alcohol, tobacco, or other drugs
- Using positive peer pressure to help counteract the negative effects of living in an environment where alcohol, tobacco, or other drug abuse or dependency exists
- Identifying ways of obtaining help to resist pressure to use alcohol, tobacco, or other drugs
- Identifying and participating in positive alternative activities, such as alcohol-, tobacco-, and drug-free events

Grade-level concepts and content	**Examples of skills and behaviors**

dents can learn and practice coping strategies that will reduce the risks. Students should know how and where to obtain help when confronted with alcohol- or drug-related problems.

Child abuse, including sexual exploitation:

Information on the neglect and abuse of children should continue to be presented. Students should be told forcefully that these problems are serious and that they may require outside assistance. After parents are notified of the forthcoming instruction, students should also be provided with information on sexual abuse and rape. In addition, students should be helped to develop skills enabling them to prevent, avoid, and cope with unwanted sexual advances and be asked to demonstrate those skills. The skills include ability to assess situations that may be dangerous; avoid those situations; avoid alcohol and other drug use; develop assertiveness skills; and learn self-defense techniques. Even when precautions are taken, however, sexual abuse or rape may occur. For that reason students should be made aware of and be given access to resources available for those who have been sexually abused, molested, or assaulted.

■ Identifying ways to seek assistance if concerned, abused, or threatened

■ Recognizing and avoiding situations that can increase risk of abuse

• Avoiding, recognizing, and responding to negative social influences and pressure to become sexually active, including applying refusal skills when appropriate

103

Grade-level concepts and content	Examples of skills and behaviors

Emergencies:

Building on the knowledge and skills learned in the elementary grades, students should explore how to develop a detailed family emergency plan and maintain safety equipment and supplies in readiness for emergencies and natural disasters. Community emergency services should be analyzed, and effective means for using them should be explored. In addition to the first-aid skills learned in the upper elementary grades, students at this level should have the opportunity to demonstrate proficiency in standard first-aid procedures, abdominal-thrust maneuver, and cardiopulmonary resuscitation (CPR). Some students may have fears about contracting a disease while administering first aid or CPR. Because some of those fears are based on myth and some on fact, students should be provided with scientific data so that they can distinguish a genuine danger from a mistaken one.

■ Recognizing emergencies and responding appropriately, including demonstrating proficiency in basic first-aid procedures, abdominal thrust maneuver, and cardiopulmonary resuscitation (CPR)

• Developing and maintaining, with other family members, a personal and family emergency plan, including maintaining supplies in readiness for emergencies

Unifying Idea:
Respect for and
promotion of the
health of others

Expectations:

1. Students will play a positive, active role in promoting the health of their families.

2. Students will promote positive health practices within the school and the community, including positive relationships with peers.

Expectation

1

Students will play a positive, active role in promoting the health of their families.

Grade-level concepts and content

Examples of skills and behaviors

Roles of family members:

Students should recognize that parenting can be a rich and rewarding experience but requires time and commitment. Parenting involves moral, social, legal, and financial responsibilities and is, therefore, an activity appropriate for responsible adults only. Parental responsibilities begin even prior to conception because health-related behavior of both parents before and during pregnancy influences the health of the baby. Although various cultures and societies have unique parenting patterns, all parents must provide for their children's development. As students explore the roles of

■ Supporting and valuing all family members

■ Demonstrating ways in which children can help support positive family interactions

■ Developing and using effective communication techniques, including talking openly and honestly with parents when problems arise and developing skills for discussing with parents questions about sexuality

■ Practicing health-promoting behaviors with the family; recognizing its role in sup-

---

■ Identifies previously introduced skills or behaviors that should be built on and reinforced.

Grade-level concepts and content	**Examples of skills and behaviors**

parents, they should recognize that balancing the responsibilities of work and parenting can be difficult. Being a responsible parent means considering this challenge and striking an appropriate balance between work and parenting. Students should also explore ways in which parental behavior affects children and focus on ways in which social, economic, and cultural factors affect family life. For example, the values or religious beliefs that parents teach and model influence how children behave. Students should recognize that traditions, history, and family pride are passed on by parents and extended family members.

One emphasis of the curriculum at this level should be on the difficulty and challenges of being a teenage parent. Teenagers are still growing and developing. Parenting responsibilities at that age can interrupt schooling, employment plans, and social and family life for both male and female teenagers. Further, the children of teenage parents often have more problems than do the children of adult parents. Birth defects, more common in children of teenage parents, are one example. In summary, teenage pregnancy can have serious effects on the teenage

porting positive health practices of others, especially younger children; and encouraging other family members to practice those positive behaviors

- Completing self-initiated activities beyond assigned chores to help support the family, such as doing the dishes without being asked
- Identifying safety hazards in the home and helping to remove those hazards

Grade-level concepts and content	*Examples of skills and behaviors*

parent, the child, the teenager's family, and society.

Students should continue to identify the skills needed to be responsible family members and should have opportunities to practice those skills. They should recognize their role in promoting the health of family members as well as preventing injuries and promoting safety at home. As students explore their roles in their families, they should recognize that the responsibilities of children change as they grown older. With adolescence usually comes greater independence and often greater responsibility.

As the child's role in the family changes, good communication with parents is particularly important. Effective communication skills can be developed that can help adolescents and their parents talk about difficult subjects in a reasonable way. Students can also explore the effects emotions have on behaviors and communication. At times a cooling-off period may be needed before conflicts can be resolved. The importance of honesty, trust, and mutual respect in family communication should be emphasized. Occasional conflicts between parents and adolescents are normal. Positive ways to resolve conflict should be a continuing emphasis of the curriculum.

Effective communication techniques include reading body language, identifying feelings, listening for feelings in the other person's communication, checking for understanding, and giving appropriate feedback on how another's behaviors and words make one feel.

107

Grade-level concepts and content	Examples of skills and behaviors

Change and the family:

Family interactions can be affected by changes in the family structure, including the results of unexpected change, disappointment, or grief. Yet there are healthy ways to deal with these emotions. Coping strategies can be developed, and family members can help each other through difficult times. Families sometimes need counseling to function well.

- Using effective strategies to cope with change in the family, such as seeking assistance from a parent, a trusted adult, a support system, or counseling when needed

Coping strategies include identifying positive and negative aspects of the change, doing something constructive to help adjust to the change, crying, accepting feelings, writing in a diary, or talking with family members and others who have had a similar experience.

Expectation

2

Students will promote positive health practices within the school and the community, including positive relationships with peers.

Grade-level concepts and content	Examples of skills and behaviors

Friendship and peer relationships:

Positive peer relationships in adolescence are a key to good health. Students should be encouraged to reach out to and include others; conversely, they should be discouraged from becoming exclusive and clique-oriented. The curriculum should focus on the need to respect the dignity of all

- Knowing and using appropriate ways to make new friends

- Demonstrating acceptable methods of gaining attention

- Demonstrating acceptable ways to show or express feelings

■ Identifies previously introduced skills or behaviors that should be built on and reinforced.

Grade-level concepts and content

people, including students and adults at school, and to avoid name calling, prejudice, exclusiveness, discrimination, and conflict. Students should be reminded that, although they may not like everyone with whom they interact, it is important to be able to communicate and work effectively with a variety of people.

Students should demonstrate decision-making and problem-solving skills to enhance interpersonal relationships and skills for building and maintaining friendships. They should be encouraged to recognize the role of positive peer relationships in encouraging healthy behaviors and discouraging risk-taking behaviors. Emphasis on skills for influencing others to avoid the use of alcohol, tobacco, and other drugs as well as other unhealthy behaviors (such as eating disorders, unsafe behaviors in and around motor vehicles, and unsafe risk-taking behaviors around bodies of water) should be continued at this level.

Because students at this level are likely to be interested in attending coeducational social activities, they should be encouraged to develop positive relationships with both males and females. Good communication is important in the devel-

Examples of skills and behaviors

- Demonstrating positive actions toward others
- Resolving conflicts in a positive, constructive way
- Demonstrating how to resist negative peer pressure
- Avoiding demeaning statements directed toward others
- Interacting effectively with many different people, including both males and females and members of different ethnic and cultural groups
- Promoting positive health behaviors among peers, including acknowledging and supporting the special health needs of others
- Helping peers know when they should seek help from a parent or other trusted adult

109

Grade-level concepts and content	**Examples of skills and behaviors**

opment of positive relationships. Communication skills and the causes and consequences of miscommunication, should be explored.

School-based and community-based efforts to promote and protect health:

As students become more aware of and involved with the larger environment, they should have opportunities to examine how laws, policies, and practices influence health locally, nationally, and internationally. The curriculum should include descriptions of how public health efforts have helped to prevent, control, and eradicate disease and how personal and public actions have affected the environment. To be included is the role of public agencies in establishing rules and laws to protect community health now and in the future.

Students can also explore and participate in efforts by school and community organizations to improve health at local, national, and international levels. This is an appropriate time to introduce information about agencies and organizations that provide protection against fraudulent health products, services, and information. The curriculum can also include a study of food

- Understanding and following school rules related to health

- Participating in school efforts to promote health

- Assuming responsibility for helping to take care of the school, such as picking up trash on the school grounds and helping other students assume responsibility for that action

- Participating in community efforts to address local health and environmental issues

- Contributing to the strengthening of health-related policies at school

- Encouraging others to become involved in health-promotion efforts at school

- Analyzing the impact of laws, policies, and practices on health-related issues

- Encouraging others to become involved in health-promotion efforts at many different levels; for example choosing not to smoke, supporting the school as a tobacco-free environment,

Grade-level concepts and content	Examples of skills and behaviors
additives, recycling, food waste, hunger, pesticide use, and the need for a safe and adequate food supply. Students should promote activities centering on disease prevention among family and friends and learn ways to assist others in making positive health decisions that have an effect on themselves and others.	and supporting local efforts to reduce smoking in the community • Accessing appropriately services available within the community

Expectations:

1. Students will understand the variety of physical, mental, emotional, and social changes that occur throughout life.

2. Students will understand and accept individual differences in growth and development.

3. Students will understand their developing sexuality, will choose to abstain from sexual activity, and will treat the sexuality of others with respect.

Expectation

1

Students will understand the variety of physical, mental, emotional, and social changes that occur throughout life.

Unifying Idea:
An understanding of the process of growth and development

Grade-level concepts and content	*Examples of skills and behaviors*

Life cycle:

Early adolescence and adolescence are times of intense change, growth, and development. They can also be times of emotional turmoil, uncertainty, anxiety, and related health and behavior problems. If not presented earlier, the changes associated with puberty and the structure and function of the male and female reproductive systems should be presented at this level. In addition to learning to understand the changes occurring during adolescence, students should be encouraged to develop strategies for coping with concerns and stress related to those changes.

- ■ Practicing good personal hygiene, paying particular attention to the changing needs of adolescents
- • Recognizing fluctuations in emotions
- ■ Managing feelings appropriately
- ■ Developing and using effective communication skills to discuss with parents or other trusted adults the changes that occur during adolescence
- • Practicing behaviors that will provide the option of healthy parenting later in life, such as avoidance of substance abuse

Expectation

2

Students will understand and accept individual differences in growth and development.

Growth and development:

At a time when students are developing in different ways and at varying rates, differences in physical, mental, emotional, and social growth and development during adolescence are an appropriate focus of the curriculum. Students should understand that

- ■ Demonstrating an understanding of individual differences
- ■ Adapting group activities to include a variety of individuals

---

■ Identifies previously introduced skills or behaviors that should be built on and reinforced.

Grade-level concepts and content	**Examples of skills and behaviors**
each individual experiences change at his or her own pace. There is no exact time frame or age for particular changes to occur. In addition, students should understand the negative impact that alcohol, tobacco, and other drugs, including performance-altering substances, have on the body and develop strategies for avoiding the use of those substances.	■ Developing a realistic body image ■ Recognizing problems associated with not having a realistic body image, including dieting and eating disorders, and seeking appropriate help • Recognizing the effects of performance-altering substances and avoiding the use of those substances

Mental and emotional development:

Although individuals vary greatly in their physical, mental, emotional, and social development, students should understand that all individuals face decisions that can influence future choices. Setting short-term and long-term goals is a helpful way of focusing and guiding one's life. While acknowledging the role of heredity in growth and development, students should be encouraged to set short-term and long-term goals related to personal health and physical fitness.	■ Identifying, expressing, and managing feelings appropriately ■ Developing and using effective communication skills ■ Recognizing one's own strengths and limitations ■ Using coping strategies, including time-management skills • Developing a focus on the future

Mental and emotional health is an important focus at this time. Students must understand and accept their rate of growth and development and be able to cope with disappointment. They must have skills and strategies for avoiding the use of alcohol, tobacco, and other drugs, such as performance-altering substances.

113

Expectation

3

Students will understand their developing sexuality, will choose to abstain from sexual activity, and will treat the sexuality of others with respect.

Grade-level concepts and content	Examples of skills and behaviors

Sexuality:

Note: The *Education Code* requires that parents be notified before any discussion of human reproductive organs and their functions and processes takes place.

Sexuality is a natural and healthy part of life. At this level it is appropriate to address the psychological, social, moral, and ethical aspects of sexuality. Students should recognize that there are differences and similarities between male and female sexuality and that the consequences of sexual involvement may differ. For example, teenage pregnancy usually has a greater impact on the female partner.

Abstinence from sexual activity should be an important theme in the curriculum at this level and should be emphasized as the wisest and healthiest choice for young people until marriage. Further, abstinence is the only totally effective method of contraception.

- Developing and using effective communication skills, including the ability to discuss with parents questions on sexuality

- Identifying appropriate ways to show affection

- Recognizing and avoiding situations that place one at risk of participating in sexual activity

- Avoiding, recognizing, and responding to negative social influences and pressure to become sexually active

- Demonstrating assertive and refusal skills and applying those skills to situations involving pressure to be sexually active

- Identifying ways to seek assistance if abused

- Practicing behaviors that support the decision to abstain from sexual activity

114

Grade-level concepts and content

All other methods of contraception carry a risk of failure in preventing unwanted teenage pregnancy. Statistics on the effectiveness or ineffectiveness of other birth-control methods in preventing unwanted pregnancies must be provided to students. Students who are considering sexual activity should be encouraged to talk with a parent or other trusted adult.

All students should be made aware that sexual feelings and desires are natural but should also be taught to recognize that they do not have to act on those feelings. They should be helped to understand that they can show affection in ways other than sexually and that love should not be equated with sexual involvement. Moreover, they must learn that it is never appropriate to force someone to have any type of intimate sexual contact.

A factual, substantiated discussion of homosexuality may be presented at this level. (*Note*: School district governing boards considering approval of such a discussion should refer to pages 51 and 186–87.) The discussion might be conducted in a limited way during or after grade seven and more fully in high school. Students should recognize, however, that most persons feel affection for both

Examples of skills and behaviors

Students can and should make a commitment to abstinence. Schools should support that commitment by teaching students the skills to maintain their commitment.

Grade-level concepts and content	Examples of skills and behaviors
men and women and that affection for someone of the same sex is not necessarily an indicator of homosexuality. Teenagers questioning their sexual orientation may be reluctant to discuss the topic for fear of reprisal. Students should respect the rights of others to seek information about homosexuality from a parent or other trusted and knowledgeable adult. Name-calling or other hurtful actions must not be tolerated. Teachers, counselors, physicians, religious leaders, and community resource centers may offer support for young people who have concerns about their sexual orientation. Religious and personal beliefs should be respected, and instruction should affirm the dignity of all individuals.	

Unifying Idea:
Informed use of health-related information, products, and services

Expectation:

Students will identify products, services, and information that may be helpful or harmful to the students' health.

Product and services:

At this level students should be encouraged to analyze in depth the range of health services in the community available from public and private organizations and agencies. They should identify

■ Identifying a variety of consumer influences and analyzing how those influences affect decisions

---

■ Identifies previously introduced skills or behaviors that should be built on and reinforced.

Grade-level concepts and content

those services that seek to prevent and treat disease. At the same time students should be encouraged to distinguish health concerns they can manage from those that require professional care. The relationship of values, socioeconomic status, and cultural experiences to the selection of health-care services should be emphasized.

Health fads and misconceptions about treatment and prevention options are appropriate for exploration, including the influence of advertising on the selection of health products and services. Students should have opportunities to contrast advertised images with real images. For example, they might counter the advertised image of youth and rugged good health or a happy cartoon character in tobacco ads with diseases caused by smoking that ravage a smoker's health.

Students should develop criteria for the selection or rejection of health products, services, and information. They should be able to analyze labels on health-related products to determine whether the products are appropriate for personal use and when they might be used. The qualifications of various health-care providers should be explored. Because the opinions of health-care professionals are not infallible, there

Examples of skills and behaviors

- Recognizing helpful products and services
- Using critical-thinking skills to analyze marketing and advertising techniques and their influence on the selection of health-related services and products
- Seeking care from the school nurse or school-linked services with families when appropriate
- Identifying appropriate sources of health services for a variety of illnesses
- Developing and applying criteria for the selection or rejection of health products, services, and information, such as determining when appropriate to take a vitamin or mineral supplement

Students should critically analyze messages in the media about sexual activity and the use of alcohol and tobacco. Recognizing false images helps negate those messages and supports students' decisions to abstain from sexual activity and the use of alcohol, tobacco, or other drugs.

Grade-level concepts and content	**Examples of skills and behaviors**

may be legitimate reasons for requesting additional information or a second opinion. Students should be able to recognize when they might wish to obtain additional information or a second opinion and analyze how to obtain this information or service. The curriculum should also include an exploration of health- and food-related careers.

Food choices:

Increasingly, students at this grade span purchase or prepare their own meals and snacks at home or away from home. They need to be aware of the variety of low-cost foods that provide nutritionally adequate diets. Information should also be provided on reliable sources of nutrition information. Students need to develop skills in identifying and responding to influences—from peers, family, friends, the media, advertising, and industry—that influence personal food choices.

Because eating disorders and fad dieting can lead to serious health problems, students should guard against becoming victims of media and peer pressures that promote an idealized and unattainable body image inappropriate for most persons. Adolescents need to be especially wary of nutri-

■ Using labels to compare the contents of food products

■ Using critical-thinking skills to analyze marketing and advertising techniques and their influence on food selection

■ Using valid nutrition information to make healthy food choices

■ Using unit pricing to determine the most economical purchases

■ Developing basic food-preparation skills, including safe and sanitary food preparation and storage

• Using effective consumer skills to purchase healthy foods within budget constraints in a variety of settings

• Using critical-thinking skills to distinguish facts from fallacies concerning the

118

Grade-level concepts and content	*Examples of skills and behaviors*
tion and health claims that promise unrealistic results.	nutritional value of foods and food supplements • Adapting recipes to make them more healthy by lowering fat, salt, or sugar and increasing fiber • Using critical thinking skills to analyze weight modification practices and selecting appropriate practices to maintain, lose, or gain weight according to individual need and scientific research

Grades Nine Through Twelve

Several principles should be kept in mind when developing health education for students in grades nine through twelve. First, although many students may seem physically mature, they are still in the process of changing from external guidance to internal direction. In addition, the illusion of immortality is common to them, and the possibility of their developing a disease or disability in the distant future may carry even less weight for them than for younger adolescents. Therefore, instruction centering on the more immediate consequences of behavior or the imminent transition to adulthood is likely to be more effective than instruction emphasizing a long-term approach. Students are receptive to information provided by trusted adults but are often overconfident about their own knowledge and coping abilities. Therefore, positive adult and peer role models are critically important at this stage.

A positive development among many students is that they are becoming aware of their influence on younger children and are taking an increasingly active role in the school and the community as concerned citizens. They are often willing participants as role models or peer advisers. By this time most students are also beginning to think about career and life options. The curriculum can stimulate those interests and help to inform students about health- or food-related careers.

1. Students will demonstrate ways in which they can enhance and maintain their own health and well-being.

2. Students will demonstrate behaviors that prevent disease and speed recovery from illness.

3. Students will practice behaviors that reduce the risk of becoming involved in potentially dangerous situations and react to such situations in ways that help to protect their health.

Expectation

1

Students will demonstrate ways in which they can enhance and maintain their own health and well-being.

Grade-level concepts and content	*Examples of skills and behaviors*

The human body:

The relationship among personal health habits, personal health, and the quality of life continues to be an important focus at this grade level. Students should develop a plan of health habits appropriate to their individual needs and analyze the ways in which personal health needs change during the life cycle. In addition, students should analyze how environmental conditions affect body systems and be able to demonstrate ways to protect

- Practicing good personal hygiene

- Using protective equipment, such as a helmet when cycling, or practicing behaviors to protect the body, such as avoiding exposure to excessive noises

- Recognizing and accepting differences in body types and maturation levels

---

■ Identifies previously introduced skills or behaviors that should be built on and reinforced.

Unifying Idea:
Acceptance of personal responsibility for lifelong health

Even at this age level, students benefit from emphasis on the importance of brushing their teeth at least twice a day and flossing daily.

Grade-level concepts and content	Examples of skills and behaviors
themselves from exposure to potentially harmful conditions.	• Responding appropriately to the physical development of older adolescents in ways that promote physical health through such preventive measures as healthy food choices and exercise

Food choices:

The curriculum should emphasize nutritional needs during the different life stages—for example, prenatal development, infancy, early childhood, adolescence, and adulthood. Individual dietary requirements vary by age, gender, health status, and level of activity. The unique nutritional needs of adolescents, including the pregnant teenagers and the school-age parent, should be particularly emphasized.

The effects of nutrition and exercise on behavior, appearance, and physical and mental performance should also be highlighted, together with the role of nutrition in preventing chronic disease. Students should develop a culturally appropriate, long-range personal nutrition plan, based on food choices and calorie levels, that promotes health and reduces the risk of disease. They should be aware of the various food sources of nutrients available in different

■ Making healthy food choices in a variety of settings

■ Establishing and maintaining healthy eating practices, including developing and using a personal nutrition plan based on food choices and calorie levels that promotes health and reduces risk of disease

■ Analyzing how food choices are influenced, including how a busy schedule influences food choices

■ Selecting appropriate practices to maintain, lose, or gain weight based on individual needs and scientific research

• Recognizing the need for updating the personal nutrition plan as individual needs or activities change and being able to do so

Students can do a "nutritional make-over" by analyzing their own activity level and what they have eaten for a week. They can then create their own recommendations for change and monitor their progress.

Grade-level concepts and content	Examples of skills and behaviors

cultural and ethnic cuisines. They should also practice healthy food-preparation skills at home, at school, and in the community.

Physical activity:

The curriculum should continue to emphasize the pleasure of physical activity. Students should be encouraged to explore a variety of activities in school and outside school. They should explore the connections between physical activity and mental and emotional health. As students plan for their transition to adulthood, they should investigate ways to maintain regular exercise practices and explore the potential harm of a sedentary life-style.

A periodic self-assessment of physical fitness should be a regular practice for students at this level. Assessment results should be used to evaluate progress toward meeting personal physical fitness goals and to refine personal fitness programs as necessary. Students should also discuss and analyze factors that influence personal motivation for participating in regular physical activity. If appropriate, they should be encouraged to develop self-motivation and self-discipline strategies to achieve

- Observing safety rules during physical activities

- Exploring ways to engage in out-of-school activities that promote health

- Participating regularly in a variety of enjoyable physical activities

- Following through with a personal fitness plan based on personal fitness goals and the results of periodic self-assessments

- Making the adjustments needed for successful implementation of the personal fitness plan, including getting additional rest when necessary

- Analyzing personal motivators related to pursuing physical activity and using those motivators to maintain ongoing participation in physical activities

- Exploring ways to continue regular exercise practices when schedules change, such as during travel or while working

Grade-level concepts and content	**Examples of skills and behaviors**

personal goals. Students should be encouraged to accept differences among individuals and recognize that different activities appeal to different individuals.

Community service activities help students build self-confidence and find joy in giving to others.

Mental and emotional health:

The mental and emotional aspects of health continue to be strongly emphasized in the curriculum at this level. Students should have opportunities to recognize and build on personal characteristics that contribute to self-confidence and self-esteem. They should understand that usually there is more than one way to solve a problem and should have opportunities to practice problem-solving skills. Students should continue to be encouraged to pursue leisure-time activities that promote physical and mental health.

The topic of suicide, introduced in middle school, can be explored in more depth at this level. Students who feel rejected or socially isolated should be encouraged to develop strategies for coping with and overcoming these feelings. Acceptable alternatives include talking over problems, understanding that feelings of depression and isolation will pass, examining the situation leading to the problem, seeking appro-

- Demonstrating personal characteristics that contribute to self-confidence and self-esteem, such as honesty, integrity, responsibility, and respect for the dignity of others

- Developing protective factors that help promote resiliency, such as developing an internal focus of control and maintaining a future focus

- Developing and using effective communication skills

- Developing and using effective coping strategies

- Avoiding self-destructive behaviors

- Practicing strategies for resisting negative peer pressure

- Identifying the strongest risk factors for negative behaviors in their own lives and developing effective strategies for counteracting the effect of those risk factors

- Selecting entertainment that promotes mental and physical health

124

Grade-level concepts and content

priate assistance if depression persists, obtaining medical treatment for organically caused depression, and participating in regular aerobic exercise. Students should understand the role of denial as a negative influence on mental and emotional health and should have opportunities to develop and use effective communication skills to overcome denial and seek assistance when needed.

Examples of skills and behaviors

- Identifying personal habits influencing mental and emotional health and developing strategies for changing behaviors as needed to promote positive mental and emotional health

- Relating in positive ways to peers and adults in and out of school

Expectation

2

Students will demonstrate behaviors that prevent disease and speed recovery from illness.

Disease prevention:

At this level students should receive more detailed information on communicable and chronic diseases and disorders. In addition, future trends and the social and economic impact of such diseases and disorders on individuals and society should be discussed. Students should learn about the major communicable and chronic diseases prevalent at different stages of life and be able to explain how the immune

- Practicing good personal hygiene to prevent the spread of disease

- Practicing positive health behaviors to reduce the risk of disease

- Cooperating in regular health screenings, including dental examinations

■ Identifies previously introduced skills or behaviors that should be built on and reinforced.

Grade-level concepts and content	*Examples of skills and behaviors*

system functions to prevent or combat disease. A variety of ways to prevent the major diseases should be described. The importance of prenatal and perinatal care and the impact of this care on both the woman and her child should also be stressed. This framework encourages emphasis on both prenatal and perinatal care so that students will understand the benefits of prenatal care to the woman and her child and the importance of care after delivery, especially for the newborn. Students should be encouraged to practice specific behaviors that support those who are ill but avoid contagion.

Continued emphasis should be given to the prevention of sexually transmitted diseases, especially HIV/AIDS. Students should compare the effectiveness of abstinence with the effectiveness or ineffectiveness of other methods of preventing sexually transmitted diseases.

The importance of regular examinations, including self-examination of the breasts or testicles, in detecting and treating diseases early should be emphasized at this time. Students should learn how to discuss procedures and test results with their health-care providers.

■ Demonstrating safely care and concern toward ill persons in the family, school, and community

■ Making a commitment to abstain from sexual activity, including exploring non-physical ways to express affection

■ Practicing and using effective self-examination procedures

• Recognizing the importance of prenatal and perinatal care

• Analyzing personal behaviors to determine how those behaviors relate to their own health and well being and the fulfillment of personal goals and how those behaviors can be modified if necessary to promote achievement of those goals

Grade-level concepts and content	Examples of skills and behaviors

Treatment of disease:

Students should be encouraged to learn ways to become fully informed about personal illness, including how to analyze the symptoms of disease and how to communicate about one's personal health with health-care providers. Family, social, economic, and cultural influences also play a role in how individuals care for personal illness. The importance of cooperating with parents and health-care providers in the treatment or management of disease should be continually emphasized. Students should also analyze the beneficial effects of medications generally and explain why it is important to take or administer prescription and over-the-counter medicines responsibly. The influence of family and cultural factors on the treatment of disease and the usefulness of participating in support groups or activities should continue to be explored.

- Recognizing symptoms of common illnesses

- Taking prescription and over-the-counter medicines properly

- Interpreting correctly the instructions written on medicine labels

- Determining when treatment of illness at home is appropriate and when and how to seek further help when needed

- Accepting responsibility for active involvement in the treatment or management of disease, including practicing and using effective communication skills to discuss illness, test results, or procedures with parents and health-care providers

- Interpreting correctly the information provided by health-care providers regarding test results or procedures

- Analyzing one's patterns related to treatment of disease to determine whether those patterns are effective and changing behaviors if necessary to facilitate management or recovery

127

Expectation

3

Students will practice behaviors that reduce the risk of becoming involved in potentially dangerous situations and will react to such situations in ways that help to protect their health.

Grade-level concepts and content	*Examples of skills and behaviors*

Potentially dangerous situations:

Because many students begin driving automobiles during this period and because young drivers are at particularly high risk of being involved in automobile accidents, they should be taught the basic rules of traffic safety as an important focus of the curriculum. Students should understand that safety requires being observant at all times because others may not follow the rules of safe driving.

Many potentially dangerous situations can be avoided or handled by the observance of safety precautions and the use of safety equipment in everyday life. Students should learn to identify hazards found in the home, the school, and the community and participate in activities to remove those hazards. They should also have the opportunity to examine what constitutes a safe versus

■ Developing and using appropriate skills to identify, avoid when possible, or cope with potentially dangerous situations

■ Practicing safe behavior in and near motorized vehicles, including observing basic traffic safety rules when driving, developing proficiency in handling a vehicle in difficult situations, wearing a seat belt, and ensuring that others wear seat belts

• Carrying emergency equipment in their vehicle

• Using latex gloves when assisting individuals who are injured

■ Practicing safe behavior in recreational activities, even in the absence of adults

---

■ Identifies previously introduced skills or behaviors that should be built on and reinforced.

128

Grade-level concepts and content	*Examples of skills and behaviors*
an unsafe neighborhood and be encouraged to participate in activities that promote neighborhood safety. A firearm is a noteworthy example of a hazardous object. Students should learn that under no circumstances should they possess or touch a firearm except under the direction of a responsible adult. Students who will be handling firearms for recreation should take a firearm-safety training course. Students should understand how to minimize the potential for injury when interacting with others who exhibit dangerous behavior. As in grades six through nine, students should be given opportunities to practice nonharmful conflict-resolution strategies and identify factors that can influence conflict resolution.	■ Practicing safe behavior in and near water ■ Using appropriate skills to avoid, resolve, and cope with conflicts ■ Understanding and following rules prohibiting possession of weapons at school ■ Reporting or obtaining assistance when faced with unsafe situations ■ Identifying factors that reduce risks of accidents and demonstrating corrective action ■ Identifying environmental factors that affect health and safety ■ Recognizing that the use of alcohol, tobacco, and other drugs plays a role in many dangerous situations ■ Demonstrating how peers can help each other avoid or cope with potentially dangerous situations in healthy ways ■ Using thinking and decision-making skills in high-risk situations involving motor vehicles and other safety hazards

Alcohol, tobacco, and other drugs:

The short-term and long-term effects associated with the use of alcohol, tobacco, and other drugs (including those	■ Exercising self-control ■ Developing and using interpersonal and other communication skills, such as

129

Grade-level concepts and content

that may alter performance, such as steroids), alone or in combination, including their effects on reproduction, pregnancy, and the health of children, should be emphasized at this level. Students should continue to explore the legal, social, and economic consequences of drug use. Instruction should continue to emphasize laws, school policies, and family rules governing the use of chemical substances. Students should also continue to develop knowledge, skills, and strategies for choosing not to use or distribute alcohol, tobacco, and other drugs. Included should be practice in ways to avoid situations involving alcohol, tobacco, and other drugs that can have a negative influence on the students' health.

Students should recognize that abuse of alcohol, tobacco, and other drugs frequently plays a role in dangerous behavior. Results of such behavior include house fires, motor-vehicle crashes, domestic violence, date rape, and the transmission of HIV/AIDS through needle sharing or sexual activity. Students should examine the influence of chemical use on driving ability, other physical tasks, and judgment and should have opportunities

Examples of skills and behaviors

assertiveness, refusal, negotiation, and conflict-resolution skills to avoid use of alcohol, tobacco, and other drugs

- Distinguishing between helpful and harmful substances

- Distinguishing between the use and misuse of prescription and nonprescription drugs

- Avoiding, recognizing, and responding to negative social influences and pressure to use alcohol, tobacco, or other drugs

- Using positive peer pressure to help counteract the negative effects of living in an environment in which abuse of or dependence on alcohol, tobacco, or other drugs is present

- Identifying ways to obtain help to resist pressures to use alcohol, tobacco, or other drugs

- Identifying and participating in positive alternatives, such as alcohol-, tobacco-, and drug-free events

- Helping to develop and support the school's no-use policy and working to support it by knowing the procedures for reporting offenses and setting a positive example

Grade-level concepts and content	Examples of skills and behaviors

to practice both refusal skills and healthy responses to high-risk situations.

Information should be provided about resources in the school and community that can help people who have alcohol-, tobacco-, or drug-related problems. The curriculum should also explore the disease concept of chemical dependencies. Students should build on their understanding of the concept that although many of the risk factors associated with alcohol and other drug use are not under the student's control, students can learn and practice coping strategies that will diminish the risks. They should analyze the role of positive coping strategies and self-respect in counteracting peer and environmental pressure to use drugs.

Child abuse, including sexual exploitation:

Neglect and child abuse should continue to be considered. Emphasis should be placed on the fact that these are serious problems that may require outside assistance. After parents are notified, students should be given information on sexual abuse and rape. Skills related to preventing, avoiding, and coping with unwanted sexual advances can be developed,

- Identifying ways to seek assistance if concerned, abused, or threatened

- Recognizing and avoiding situations that can increase risk of abuse, including avoiding the use of alcohol and other drugs

- Avoiding, recognizing, and responding to negative social influences and pressure to become sexually active,

131

Grade-level concepts and content	*Examples of skills and behaviors*
and students should demonstrate those skills. Even when precautions are taken, however, a rape may occur. Students should be aware of and be able to obtain help provided for those who have been sexually abused, molested, or assaulted.	including applying refusal skills when appropriate ■ Developing and using assertiveness skills and learning self-defense techniques

Emergencies:

If not learned earlier, cardiopulmonary resuscitation (CPR) and other first-aid procedures for life-threatening emergencies should be mastered at this level. In addition to the skills listed at previous grade levels, instruction should include caring for victims of severe insect stings and snakebites as well as learning how to administer first aid to persons with broken bones and how to transport victims properly. The personal and legal responsibilities of individuals involved in emergencies should be explored and analyzed. Students should continue to work with their families to identify and remove safety hazards in the home, develop and maintain a detailed family emergency plan, and maintain safety equipment and supplies for emergencies and natural disasters. Emergency supplies should be maintained at home and in vehicles. Students and	■ Recognizing emergency situations and responding appropriately ■ Developing and maintaining, with other family members, a personal and family emergency plan, including maintaining supplies in readiness for emergencies, including supplies at home and supplies in their vehicle • Identifying appropriate use of local emergency services • Using latex gloves when assisting individuals who are injured

Family emergency plans can save lives, and students can play an important role in developing those plans.

132

Grade-level concepts and content	Examples of skills and behaviors

their families should discuss what they would do if one or more family members were away from home during an emergency and include plans for coping with this situation in their family emergency plan. They should analyze local emergency services and determine the appropriate (and inappropriate) use of those services.

Expectations:

1. Students will play a positive, active role in promoting the health of their families.

2. Students will promote positive health practices within the school and the community, including positive relationships with peers.

Expectation

1

Students will play a positive, active role in promoting the health of their families.

Roles of family members:

Building on the information presented at earlier levels, students at this level should continue to explore family development and the factors that help families to stay strong and healthy, including the sharing of a variety of family

- Supporting and valuing all family members
- Demonstrating ways in which adolescents can help support positive family interactions

---

■ Identifies previously introduced skills or behaviors that should be built on and reinforced.

Unifying Idea:
Respect for and promotion of the health of others

Doing things as a family helps strengthen family ties. At a time when many adolescents are busy with their own lives, encouraging time for family activities or time with a trusted adult reinforces the importance of spending time with other generations and learning from their experience and perspective.

Grade-level concepts and content

experiences and traditions. Family communication remains an important area to emphasize, especially in light of the growing independence of adolescents.

Strong families help their members reach their fullest potential. Ways of strengthening families include continually emphasizing, within the family, ways to support and respect all family members, effective approaches for solving family problems, and strategies for dealing with crisis and change. As adolescents develop more independence from their parents, they may exhibit or be tempted to exhibit individual behavior that conflicts with their family's standards. Students should understand how this behavior can affect the family and practice family communication skills and related approaches to solving family problems and conflicts. Instruction at this level should emphasize that family members can have conflicts while continuing to love and support each other.

Students should analyze short-term and long-term effects that the abuse of alcohol, tobacco, or other drugs can have on the roles and relationships within the family. For example, some students at this

Examples of skills and behaviors

■ Developing and using effective communication techniques

■ Practicing health-promoting behaviors with the family; recognizing their role in supporting positive health practices of others, especially younger children; and encouraging other family members to practice those positive behaviors

■ Completing self-initiated activities beyond assigned chores to help support the family

■ Identifying safety hazards in the home and helping to remove them

• Seeking assistance if living in a family where abuse of alcohol, or other drugs exists (e.g., participating in a support groups for teens who are the children of alcoholics)

134

Grade-level concepts and content	*Examples of skills and behaviors*

age may take on roles inappropriate for their age but necessary because of family structure. For example, the oldest child of alcoholic parents may assume responsibility for monitoring and disciplining younger siblings.

Love, cooperation, and mutual respect are universal qualities that contribute to good family functioning. Students should be encouraged to develop those qualities.

Change and the family:

The effects of change on family interactions continue to be important at this grade span. The curriculum may include the influence of religious or cultural beliefs on family interactions. For example, students might analyze the process of grieving in various cultures. In addition, they should investigate their upcoming transition to independent living, critique their skills related to this transition, and create a plan to help develop those skills necessary for a successful transition. Students should also explore how the aging process affects families and should understand their role in helping their parents assist grandparents.

■ Using effective strategies to cope with change in the family

• Developing a plan to facilitate transition from the role as a child to the role of an independent adult and discussing the plan with one's parents while it is being developed

• Discussing with parents plans to continue education beyond high school and developing a mutual understanding of how this change will affect family roles and interactions

Expectation

2

Students will promote positive health practices within the school and the community, including positive relationships with peers.

Grade-level concepts and content	Examples of skills and behaviors

Friendship and peer relationships:

Students should understand the responsibilities of being a **good** friend—and accept that the responsibility means encouraging their friends to behave in ways which enhance their health.

An important emphasis of the curriculum at this level is the need to respect the dignity of all people. Students should demonstrate ability to interact effectively with a wide range of individuals at school and should encourage others to behave in similar positive ways toward others. It will be important to distinguish between one's own feelings about the opinions or behaviors of other people and the need to respect others' rights and individuality. That is, students should realize that one can disagree with others and still interact effectively with them.

Students should understand the importance of their personal standards being consistent with their behavior. They should demonstrate decision-making and problem-solving skills to enhance interpersonal relationships as well as skills for building and maintaining friendships. Positive, healthy

- Knowing and using appropriate ways to make new friends
- Demonstrating positive actions toward others
- Resolving conflicts in a positive, constructive way
- Demonstrating how to resist negative peer pressure
- Interacting effectively with many different people, including both males and females and members of different ethnic and cultural groups
- Avoiding demeaning statements directed toward others
- Promoting positive health behaviors among peers
- Participating in group activities as a means of getting to know other people
- Analyzing appropriate behaviors in a dating relationship
- Respecting the dignity of the persons with whom they

| *Grade-level concepts and content* | *Examples of skills and behaviors* |

friendships reinforce one's sense of self-worth. Students should recognize the role of responsible companions in encouraging healthy behavior and discouraging unhealthy risk-taking, including strategies for influencing others to avoid the use of alcohol, tobacco, and other drugs as well as other negative behaviors.

Developing new friendships and new social skills with males and females should also be emphasized. Students should continue to develop and enhance their communication skills and skills for building and maintaining friendships. Group activities should be encouraged that allow teenagers to learn about others without dating. Students should recognize that people date for different reasons, that not all teenagers date, and that parents usually decide at what age their children may start dating. As they develop friendships, students can begin to identify criteria that might be used later in life to select a mate.

Honor and respect for monogamous, heterosexual marriage should be an important emphasis of the curriculum at this level. Students should be able to contrast a dating relationship with a marriage relationship. Dating can be a way to learn about other

interact, including dates, and expecting that their own dignity will be treated with respect

- Respecting monogamous, heterosexual marriage

137

Grade-level concepts and content	**Examples of skills and behaviors**

people, about romantic feelings and expressions, and about what it is like to be in a love relationship. Marriage is a legal commitment that a man and a woman make to share their lives and family responsibilities. It requires dedication and perseverance. A successful marriage requires good interpersonal skills and the ability to make adjustments to meet the needs of another person. The importance of open communication, respect, honesty, and monogamy in marriage should be emphasized.

School and community-based efforts to promote and protect health:

Building on their earlier study, students should evaluate local, national, and international efforts for preventing, controlling, and eradicating disease, hunger, and pollution. They should have opportunities to analyze how public health policies and laws are developed and to examine the role of interest groups and individual advocacy in this process and the importance of voting. Students should examine how nations share responsibility for the health of all people; for example, international response to disasters can be explored. In addition, they may initiate or participate in developing

- Understanding and following school rules related to health
- Participating in school efforts to promote health
- Assuming responsibility for helping to take care of the school and helping other students assume responsibility for that task
- Participating in community efforts to address local health and environmental issues, such as volunteer work at hospitals, food banks, childcare centers, centers for persons recovering from

Grade-level concepts and content	*Examples of skills and behaviors*
school and community efforts to prevent and control disease. Community responsibility for health promotion can also be explored through an analysis of the efforts of local government and community groups and organizations. Students should also identify the psychosocial needs of those who are disabled or ill and analyze the services provided by community organizations and agencies in meeting these needs. For example, students might explore the services available to support patients afflicted by Alzheimer's disease and their families. Specific strategies for involving others in safely demonstrating care and concern for people who are ill should be included. Students should recognize that while anyone can become disabled, disabilities are not contagious. Students can also analyze laws and standards related to food, food handling, an adequate food supply, the environment, and agriculture. They can become active in environmental and economic issues that affect the food supply and the nutritional quality of food.	trauma, or centers for persons with disabilities ■ Encouraging others to become involved in health-promotion efforts at school ■ Analyzing the influence of laws, policies, and practices on health-related issues, including those related to food and nutrition ■ Encouraging others to become involved in health-promotion efforts at many different levels ■ Accessing appropriately those services available within the community • Initiating and involving others in health-promotion efforts at school or in the community

Unifying Idea:
An under-standing of the process of growth and development

Expectations:

1. Students will understand the variety of physical, mental, emotional, and social changes that occur throughout life.

2. Students will understand and accept individual differences in growth and development.

3. Students will understand their developing sexuality, will choose to abstain from sexual activity, and will treat the sexuality of others with respect.

Expectation

1

Students will understand the variety of physical, mental, emotional, and social changes that occur throughout life.

Grade-level concepts and content	Examples of skills and behaviors

Life cycle:

The various stages of life, including pregnancy, infancy, childhood, adolescence, young adulthood, middle age, and older adulthood should be investigated by students at this time. Students should recognize that a variety of physical, mental, emotional, and social changes occur throughout life and that although there are predictable stages of a human being's life cycle, individuals develop and mature at their own rate. An individual's ability to make adjustments

■ Developing and using effective communication skills to discuss with parents or other trusted adults the changes that occur during adolescence

■ Practicing behaviors that will provide for healthy parenting later in life, such as avoidance of substance abuse

• Recognizing and being prepared to adapt to the changes that occur during life, such as changes associ-

---

■ Identifies previously introduced skills or behaviors that should be built on and reinforced.

| *Grade-level concepts and content* | *Examples of skills and behaviors* |

while passing through the various stages of life can significantly influence the quality of that life. Students should explore changes during the life cycle, including normal bodily growth and development, and physical changes caused by diseases and injuries. They should investigate the influence of food choices on the various stages of life and on recovery from diseases and injuries. Students should also analyze how such skills as the ability to cope, adjust, make decisions, communicate feelings, make and keep friends, care for others, and show concern for the community influence individuals through the various stages of life.

This level is appropriate for emphasizing the reproductive process and fetal development from conception through pregnancy to birth. The curriculum should address the role of prenatal care and proper nutrition in promoting optimal health for both the baby and the mother. Instruction should also emphasize the importance of a woman consulting a health-care provider if she suspects she is pregnant. The harmful effects of certain substances on the fetus (e.g., alcohol, tobacco, and other drugs as well as environmental hazards such as lead) should be emphasized, includ-

ated with young adulthood, pregnancy, middle age, or old age

- Recognizing and acknowledging that different people progress through different stages of the life cycle at different rates

- Expressing support and compassion for others who are grieving, including allowing their friends to be sad and to express their feelings

- Recognizing questions they have regarding death and dying and discussing these questions with parents, religious leaders, and other trusted adults

- Reviewing family histories and determining whether a genetic disorder exists in the family

Grade-level concepts and content	*Examples of skills and behaviors*
ing the periods during which the fetus is most susceptible to developing birth defects. Genetic disorders and conditions can also cause birth defects. Fortunately, they can often be identified when they occur in families. Some genetic disorders are so serious that they may influence one's decision to become a parent. In that event a couple may wish to consider adoption. Care of a newborn, including the importance of immunizations and well-baby care, may also be discussed at this time.	
Because death and dying are a part of the life cycle and the death of others is a part of everyone's experience, students should have an opportunity to explore death and dying. Normal emotions associated with death and dying include fear, discomfort, concern, and nervousness. After a death and other types of loss, people may feel grief, anger, resentment, abandonment, fear, despair, pain, guilt, acceptance, or relief. In time one progresses through the mourning process, and feelings of grief usually diminish. Not everyone, however, experiences the same mourning process. The stages of the process may include denial, anger, bargaining, depression, and acceptance.	

Expectation

2

Students will understand and accept individual differences in growth and development.

| Grade-level concepts and content | Examples of skills and behaviors |

Growth and development:

A continuing emphasis on individual differences in physical, mental, and social growth and development is appropriate at this level. Students should understand that individuals experience changes and stages at their own pace.

Adolescents, especially adolescent athletes, are often preoccupied with attaining an idealized body size and shape and are particularly susceptible to nutrition quackery, eating disorders, and the lure of performance-enhancing substances, such as steroids. The curriculum should continue to emphasize the importance of basing personal nutrition and fitness plans on valid scientific data. Students need to be reminded that a wide range of body types is normal and that trying to conform to an idealized image is not only unrealistic but may be unhealthy. Desperate attempts to lose weight to conform to a culturally defined body shape and

- Demonstrating an understanding of individual differences
- Adapting group activities to include a variety of individuals
- Developing a realistic body image
- Recognizing health, nutrition, and psychological problems associated with not having a realistic body image, including dieting and eating disorders, and seeking appropriate help
- Recognizing the effects of performance-altering substances and avoiding the use of those substances
- Promoting acceptance of a range of body types and abilities
- Using scientific data as a basis for individual nutrition and fitness plans

---

■ Identifies previously introduced skills or behaviors that should be built on and reinforced.

Students should recognize the dangers associated with trying to attain an idealized body size and shape. Students should avoid developing eating disorders and using performance-enhancing substances, such as steroids.

Grade-level concepts and content	Examples of skills and behaviors

size may result in eating disorders that require professional treatment.

Mental and emotional development:

Setting long-term goals for oneself as a way of focusing and guiding one's life can be a particularly effective strategy at this level. While acknowledging the role of heredity in growth and development, students should be encouraged to set immediate and long-term personal health and physical fitness goals. As they develop long-term goals, students should recognize that almost all students can expect to spend at least part of their adult lives in the work force. Increasingly, jobs and careers of every description are open to qualified individuals regardless of gender.

Students should have the opportunity to explore the expectation of tragedy or loss in their lives and examine successful coping strategies. Events such as the loss of a loved one or a serious illness in the family will be experienced by most people at some point in their lives. Students can discuss coping strategies, such as receiving support from family members, drawing strength from religious beliefs, or seeking assistance from friends or a

- Identifying, expressing, and managing feelings appropriately
- Developing and using effective communication skills
- Recognizing one's own strengths and limitations
- Using coping strategies, including time-management skills
- Developing a focus on the future

144

Grade-level concepts and content	*Examples of skills and behaviors*

counselor, and can determine which coping strategies would be most effective in helping them through a difficult time.

Expectation

3

Students will understand their developing sexuality, will choose to abstain from sexual activity, and will treat the sexuality of others with respect.

Note: The *Education Code* requires that parents be notified before human reproductive organs and their functions and processes are discussed.

Sexuality:

A strong emphasis on abstinence should be continued at this grade span. Students should be encouraged to make a commitment to abstain from sexual activity until they are ready for marriage. Even those who have already engaged in sexual intercourse can choose to be abstinent. However, contraceptive methods and their relative effectiveness and ineffectiveness should be discussed. Instruction should emphasize that abstinence is the only totally effective method of contraception and that all other methods carry a risk of failure in preventing unwanted teenage pregnancy

■ Developing and using effective communication skills, including the ability to discuss with parents questions regarding sexuality

■ Identifying appropriate ways to show affection

■ Recognizing and avoiding situations that place one at risk of participating in sexual activity

■ Avoiding, recognizing, and responding to negative social influences and pressure to become sexually active

---

■ Identifies previously introduced skills or behaviors that should be built on and reinforced.

To support students in making a commitment to abstinence, include an experiential component in the curriculum at this level to provide (1) guided rehearsal of refusal skills to resist sexual abuse or unwanted sexual advances; (2) opportunities to practice using healthy responses; and (3) information about where to seek help or get answers to one's questions.

Grade-level concepts and content

and sexually transmitted diseases. The consequences of unwanted pregnancies and the effects of teenage pregnancy on the teenagers, their child, their parents, and society should also be explored.

Students should be made aware that sexual feelings and desires are natural but that they do not have to act on those feelings. Sexual feelings, love, and intimacy are distinct aspects of sexual attraction. Responsible sexual behavior can and should be defined. Students who date should discuss limits with their dating partners and should expect those partners to respect those limits. Even when tempted to engage in sexual activity, students can exercise self-control.

A factual, substantiated discussion of homosexuality may be included at this level. (*Note*: School district governing boards considering such a discussion should see pages 51 and 186–87.) Students should recognize that it is a common experience to feel some affection for both men and women and that feelings of affection for persons of the same sex are not necessarily an indication of homosexuality. Teenagers who have questions about their sexual orientation may be reluctant to discuss the topic for

Examples of skills and behaviors

- Demonstrating assertive and refusal skills and applying those skills to situations involving pressure to be sexually active
- Identifying ways to seek assistance if abused
- Practicing behaviors that support the decision to abstain from sexual activity, including self-control, use of reason as a basis for action, self-discipline, a sense of responsibility, religious convictions, or ethical considerations
- Analyzing messages about sexuality from society, including the media, identifying how those messages affect behavior
- Evaluating what students can do to counteract the false norms portrayed in the media

Grade-level concepts and content	*Examples of skills and behaviors*

fear of reprisal. Students should respect the rights of others to seek information from a parent or other trusted and knowledgeable adult. Name-calling or other hurtful actions must not be tolerated. Teachers, counselors, physicians, religious leaders, and community resource centers may offer support for young people who have concerns about their sexual orientation. While respecting religious and personal beliefs, the curriculum in this content area should affirm the dignity of all individuals.

Physical, mental, social, and cultural factors influence attitudes and behaviors regarding sexuality. Attitudes about proper behavior for men and women differ among families and cultures. Gender stereotypes may influence behavior, career paths, relationships, and so on, but these stereotypes do not have to be accepted. Social messages about sexuality may be confusing and contradictory. False images of sexual behavior are often portrayed in the media. Students should have opportunities to explore and analyze the effects of social and cultural influences on human sexuality.

Name-calling and other hurtful actions must not be tolerated.

147

Unifying Idea:
Informed use of health-related information, products, and services

Learning how to make a medical appointment, fill out medical question-naires and billing forms, and analyze different kinds of insurance coverage helps students understand the need to be well-informed, analytical consumers.

Expectation:

Students will identify products, services, and information that may be helpful or harmful to their health.

Grade-level concepts and content	**Examples of skills and behaviors**

Products and services:

At this level it is especially important that students, many of whom will receive no further instruction in health education, become informed health consumers. Students' failure to become informed can have a negative influence not only on the students but on all of society as well. The health-care system is a product of our society's cumulative economic and political choices. Students can help to improve this system by becoming well-informed, careful consumers. To do so requires students to learn that there are primary points of entry for obtaining health care, including preventive, diagnostic, and treatment services, and that it is important to have an established source for primary care, rather than depend on an emergency room.

Students should be able to apply criteria for selecting health services, products, and information. For example, students might analyze major types of health-insurance coverage and develop criteria for selecting health insurance. Or they might analyze how to

■ Identifying a variety of consumer influences and analyzing how those influences affect decisions

■ Recognizing helpful products and services

■ Using critical-thinking skills to analyze marketing and advertising techniques and their influence on the selection of health-related services and products

■ Seeking care from the nurse's office or school-linked services with their families when appropriate

■ Identifying appropriate sources of health services for a variety of illnesses and being able to use those services

■ Developing and applying criteria for the selection or rejection of health products, services, and information, including products or services designed to enhance physical fitness, such as exercise gear

---

■ Identifies previously introduced skills or behaviors that should be built on and reinforced.

148

Grade-level concepts and content	Examples of skills and behaviors
access public and private health services by learning how to make appointments and complete health and insurance forms. The costs and benefits of health products, services, and information can also be analyzed. Students should develop strategies for identifying and combating fraudulent health products, services, and information. They should also continue to analyze the influence of advertising, especially targeted advertising, on the selection of health products and services. The legal rights of individuals to obtaining health care services should also be explored. Many avenues are available to students at this level for pursuing community service experiences related to health care and prevention. Voluntary health-care organizations offer one way to introduce students to educational and other resources in the community through which they can contribute to the support of community health needs.	• Using critical-thinking skills to analyze the cost benefits of health care products and services • Developing and using strategies for identifying and combating fraudulent or misleading health products, services, and information

Food choices:

As high school students become more skilled consumers, they need to be able to understand the factors that influence the cost, quality, availability, and variety of food	■ Using labels to compare the contents of food products ■ Using critical-thinking skills to analyze marketing and advertising techniques and

149

Grade-level concepts and content	Examples of skills and behaviors
in the marketplace locally, nationally, and internationally. To be skilled consumers, students also need to be able to evaluate nutrition information. Many nutritional claims, products, and so-called research are deceptive and can lead to serious adverse health consequences. Students need to know how and where to obtain valid, reliable information on nutrition.	their influence on food selection ■ Using valid nutrition information to make healthy food choices ■ Using unit pricing to determine the most economical purchases ■ Using effective consumer skills to purchase healthy foods within budget constraints and in a variety of settings ■ Using critical-thinking skills to distinguish facts from fallacies concerning the nutritional value of foods and food supplements ■ Adapting recipes to make them more healthy by lowering the amount of fat, salt, or sugar and increasing the amount of fiber • Using critical-thinking skills to analyze weight modification practices and selecting appropriate practices to maintain, lose, or gain weight according to individual need and scientific research

Chapter 4

Beyond Health Education

Central to an effective comprehensive school health system is a carefully planned approach to developing and reinforcing health literacy in students. Health education and the comprehensive school health system offer abundant opportunities for everyone in the school and the community to become involved in a collaborative undertaking. This chapter offers a variety of ways in which that reinforcement and involvement can take place.

The participation of a wide range of adults in the school and the community is an essential element of a successful comprehensive school health system. The principal, the faculty, the support staff, the parents—everyone in the school—must recognize children's health as an important priority. A schoolwide focus on health ensures that emphasis will be placed on developing and sustaining healthy behaviors. If the environment of the school and the community does not reinforce healthy behaviors and choices, students may perceive that such behaviors and choices are not uniformly valued. For example, although students may, through the health curriculum, learn about the importance of a balanced diet, their behavior may be undermined by the easy availability of nonnutritious foods in hallway vending machines or at school-sponsored activities. Similarly, although the importance of regular aerobic physical activity may be emphasized in health education and physical education classes, many adults at the school may remain inactive. A mixed message about health and a lack of adult role modeling and support for health literacy can undermine the best health education program.

Components of a Comprehensive School Health System

This chapter focuses on how schools can build a comprehensive school health system to support and reinforce instruction on healthy behavior and health literacy. A comprehensive school health system consists of eight components:

- Health Education
- Physical Education

- Health Services
- Nutrition Services
- Psychological and Counseling Services
- Health Promotion for Staff
- Safe and Healthy School Environment
- Parent and Community Involvement

Health Education

Health education, described in detail in Chapter 3, should be comprehensive and multidimensional and should not be limited to classroom exercises, textbook readings, or seat work. It should promote active student involvement, critical thinking, development and reinforcement of positive health behaviors, and a variety of engaging health-related projects both in and out of school. To complement the description of health education, the following discussion focuses on the other seven components of a comprehensive school health system—how they are interrelated and how they can be supported and strengthened.

Physical Education

Physical education should provide all students with opportunities to participate in a comprehensive, sequentially planned physical education program. Through movement physical education advances the physical, mental, emotional, and social well-being of every individual in the pursuit of lifelong health. Students should have opportunities to develop and enhance their movement skills and their understanding of how their body moves and should participate in a variety of activities leading to lifelong enjoyment of physical activity. Physical education for children in kindergarten through grade twelve is the subject of another

Ten Benefits of Comprehensive School Health Systems

1. *Less school vandalism*
2. *Improved attendance by students and staff*
3. *Reduced health care costs*
4. *Reduced substitute teaching costs*
5. *Better family communications, even on sensitive issues, such as sexuality*
6. *Stronger self-confidence and self-esteem*
7. *Noticeably fewer students using tobacco*
8. *Improved cholesterol levels for students and staff*
9. *Increased use of seat belts*
10. *Improved physical fitness*

—Healthy Kids for the Year 2000: An Action Plan for Schools

framework. Detailed information on the design of an effective physical education curriculum is provided in the *Physical Education Framework.*[1]

Health Services

Health services are those health-related procedures, screenings, or referrals coordinated at the school site by the credentialed school nurse or school-linked service providers. The nature and extent of health services vary from place to place. In general, however, all schools should be prepared to:

1. Treat minor illness and injuries, provide routine first aid, and assist in medical emergencies.

2. Identify and help manage the care of students with chronic conditions.

3. Conduct preventive health screenings, such as those for vision, hearing, or detection of scoliosis.

4. Refer the family to health providers in the community when problems are detected and do the necessary follow-up with the family as needed.

5. Keep up-to-date records of immunizations and health status.

According to the National Association of School Nurses, an acceptable nurse-to-student ratio is generally 1:750 but lower in schools with a concentration of special needs students.[2] Most schools in California do not have a full-time nurse of their own. Often, a nurse or nurse practitioner spends time at two or more schools and may have to supervise one or more on-site health aides. This failure to provide adequate nursing

The school nurse is an invaluable asset to a comprehensive school health system and represents a highly cost-effective community investment in the prevention of health problems.

[1] *Physical Education Framework for California Public Schools, Kindergarten Through Grade Twelve.* Sacramento: California Department of Education, 1994.

[2] *Resolutions and Policy Statements.* Scarborough, Me.: National Association of School Nurses, 1990 p. 22.

154

is regrettable because the school nurse is an invaluable asset to a comprehensive school health system and represents a highly cost-effective community investment in the prevention of health problems.

Another approach to providing health services and support to families can be found in the growing number of school-based or school-linked health services. These services may be offered by public health agencies or the school district and may be funded by a combination of public and private funds. In some communities school health clinics and school-linked services provide a range of health and support services, such as immunizations and acute care for infections, to students who might otherwise go without medical care and offer an excellent opportunity for school-community collaboration. The decision to provide school-linked support services and the guidelines for operating them are sensitive matters that should be determined by the local community and the school district governing board.

Nutrition Services

An effective nutrition services program is basic to successful learning in schools. Hungry children can neither learn nor achieve their potential in physical development, level of activity, or mental ability. Nutrition services can help to alleviate the physical signs and behaviors related to hunger and improve resistance to some communicable diseases. In addition, when received by pregnant teenagers, these services help to reduce the risk of developmental disabilities and greatly reduce infant mortality, a serious problem in teenage pregnancy. Depending on the needs of the students and the community, nutrition services might include breakfast and lunch programs, a summer feeding program, a pregnant and lactating teen program, a special milk program, and a child-care food program.

U ndernutrition increases the risk and severity of illnesses, and iron deficiency anemia results in shortened attention span, fatigue, and decreased ability to concentrate. Child nutrition programs, such as the lunch and breakfast programs and other food supplement programs, may help improve the nutritional status— and readiness to learn—of California's children.

A national health goal is that at least 90 percent of the school lunch and breakfast programs provide food choices consistent with such dietary recommendations as those contained in *The California Daily Food Guide*.[3] Specifically, the goal is to increase the consumption of whole grains, fruits, and vegetables and moderate the consumption of fat, salt, sugar, and empty-calorie foods. In addressing this goal, nutrition services can offer students a variety of foods that promote optimal health while reflecting student preferences. However, the school nutrition program does more than feed students; it functions as a living laboratory for the practice of good eating habits learned in the classroom. Nutrition services personnel can also be an invaluable resource to the classroom, providing assistance in nutrition-related lessons.

Psychological and Counseling Services

Psychological and counseling services at the school site provide students with support and assistance in making healthy decisions, managing emotions, coping with crises, and setting short-term and long-term goals. Symptoms of mental, emotional, and social problems may be especially apparent among adolescents, ranging from abuse of alcohol, tobacco, and other drugs to eating disorders, antisocial aggression, and suicidal depression. Early detection of mental and emotional problems among children in elementary school should also be an important priority. Further, psychological and counseling services can provide support to students and their families after disasters or violent occurrences at or near the school.

---

[3] *The California Daily Food Guide: Dietary Guidance for Californians*. Sacramento: California Department of Education, 1990. Ordering information can be found at the back of this publication.

Every school should have a well-coordinated and fully supported program led by a certificated professional who can help identify students with high-risk behaviors and intervene early with necessary assistance to parents and referrals to appropriate agencies. The primary responsibility for these services should be assigned to a professional counselor whose time should not be monopolized by administrative duties. However, because student health is a schoolwide concern, every adult on campus should watch out for troubled youngsters and assist them in finding the help and support they need.

Health Promotion for Staff

Part of the value of a staff health-promotion program lies in the numerous personal benefits it can offer staff members. Consistent with the growing number of health and fitness programs supported by private industry, schools should view health promotion for staff as part of an overall approach to disease prevention and sound health policy. In addition, adults must view themselves as role models for healthy behavior if they are serious about helping young people achieve health literacy.

School-based health and fitness programs for staff members and other adults can take many forms, including work-site health promotion programs; health-risk appraisals; personal goal-setting sessions; support groups; employee assistance programs; and classes in aerobics, stress management, weight control, and smoking cessation. The common denominator throughout is teaching by example and promoting the health of all adults in the school.

Adults must view themselves as role models for healthy behavior if they are serious about helping young people achieve health literacy.

Safe and Healthy School Environment

This component relates to the physical and emotional environments of the school. Above all, a safe and healthy school environment ensures that the school is a haven from the violence many young people encounter elsewhere. Such an environment is one that is well maintained and is free of such hazards as asbestos dust or drinking water contaminated by lead. A plan to be implemented in case of fire or natural disasters or other emergencies should be provided and should be well rehearsed. In addition, lavatories and other sanitary facilities should be kept clean, supplied with soap and towels, and maintained well; play equipment should be inspected for safety at regular intervals; and the school grounds should be monitored and kept free of alcohol, tobacco, and other drugs.

The human side of a safe and healthy environment is less tangible but just as important. It involves effective leadership and a sense of collaboration and community. Healthy schools are characterized by a culture of concern and mutual support among staff members and students. The importance of social values—caring for others, treating others with respect, affirming diversity, and being a responsible member of a group—should be clearly stated, recognized, and modeled by all adults. Demeaning statements or actions directed to staff members or students should not be tolerated.

Parent and Community Involvement

Involving families and the local community in the comprehensive school health system is essential to encouraging

Above all, a safe and healthy school environment ensures that the school is a haven from the violence many young people encounter elsewhere.

positive health behaviors in children. Family values and community norms help shape the health decisions of young people. It follows, then, that if schools are to promote children's health literacy, they must reach out to key influence groups in the community. Working together, the school, the family, and the community can tailor the comprehensive school health system to meet the school's specific needs.

Although the school receives support from family members in many different ways, it must uphold the role of the parent or guardian as the child's primary caretaker. To do so includes understanding and respecting the different ways in which families and cultural and ethnic groups may view health-related issues. It also includes a recognition that the law provides parents with basic rights regarding the review of certain health-related instructional materials and the option of removing their children from those parts of instructional programs dealing with health, family life education, or sex education that conflict with the parents' religious training or beliefs.[4]

The role of the family is paramount in each child's development. Parents want to support the mission of the schools and will do so most effectively when they are involved in a decision-making partnership with the local school.

—It's Elementary!

Interrelationships of Components

Each component of a comprehensive school health system has its own characteristics and involves adults possessing distinct professional orientation and specialized skills. To view the components as completely independent and separate from each other, is however, inconsistent with the philosophy of a comprehensive school health system and is counterproductive.

Taken together, all eight components make up a comprehensive school health system. All relate to the development of

[4] See Appendix A for pertinent *Education Code* sections.

The comprehensive school health system creates unity, coherence, and consistent support for students' health literacy.

health literacy in students, and all are important. The more school health planners can establish connections and interrelationships among the components, the stronger will be the overall comprehensive school health system and the more positive will be the outcomes for children's health. A well-integrated system creates unity, coherence, and consistent support for students' health literacy. Rather than being limited to discrete time slots labeled *health*, the system permeates the school day. It is schoolwide, involving students and adults within the school and in the community.

The following discussion of connections and interrelationships focuses on two key aspects of organizing the comprehensive school health system; that is, linkages within the school and linkages between the school and the community. Both are important to a successful comprehensive school health system. Throughout, examples are used to illustrate ways in which interrelationships can be established and reinforced; however, they are not intended to constitute a complete or exhaustive list. Because there is no single correct way to organize a school health effort, specifics will vary from one setting to another.

Creating Linkages Within the School

The most important principle for organizing and establishing relationships among the components of a comprehensive school health system is the same as it is for health education; that is, interrelationships should be guided by the four unifying

160

ideas of health literacy. All eight components should reinforce each other and complement the ways in which the unifying ideas are used to guide health education. Examples include the following:

Accepting Personal Responsibility

- The *physical education* program can emphasize the development of individual skills and talents and a positive attitude toward physical activity that contributes to lifelong health and fitness. Physical educators can encourage students to participate in physical activities and develop skills and talents involving movement and dance that can be used throughout their lives. By emphasizing children's abilities to meet physical challenges and stay physically fit, physical education can help to enhance the relationship between acceptance of responsibility for one's physical well-being and consequent self-esteem.

- Accepting personal responsibility requires, among other things, an ability to gain access to and use *health services* when necessary or appropriate. The school nurse and school-linked health-care providers can play a role in reinforcing personal responsibility by encouraging students to learn more about the functioning of their bodies through periodic health screenings and treatment of minor injuries. Personal responsibility involves self-diagnostic skills—knowing, for example, whether and when it is important to see the school nurse or another health-care provider. Students who take regu-

Health-literate individuals acknowledge that they have some control over their health, incorporate health-related knowledge into everyday behavior, and make a lifelong commitment to healthy living.

lar medication will interact with the school nurse and may also need the assistance of the nurse from time to time.

- The *nutrition services* program can and should offer students a wide range of healthy food choices. Beyond choosing the food they eat, students can be encouraged to contribute to and design menus, focusing on healthy ingredients and varied methods of food preparation.

- *Health promotion for staff* can provide role modeling for students when the adults in the school demonstrate personal responsibility for their health and well-being. Joint staff-student games and physical activities can help to promote the idea that health and fitness are enjoyable pursuits for people of all ages.

Respecting and Promoting the Health of Others

- *Physical education* can reinforce respect for and promotion of the health of others by promoting an understanding of individual differences, effective teamwork, and cooperation. An important outgrowth of an effective physical education program is the development of positive, healthy relationships in children.

- Promotion of a *safe and healthy school environment* is particularly important in reinforcing respect for and promotion of others' health. The culture of the school should be one that values respect and caring for others and social and civic responsibility. One application of this culture of concern for others would be to make a safe and healthy school environment accessible to all. To do so, some schools

Health-literate individuals understand and acknowledge the effects of personal behavior on the health and well-being of others.

162

may have to provide devices and facilities for those who are blind or deaf or are confined to wheel-chairs.

- *Nutrition services* can encourage students to recognize the importance of healthy foods and menus for all students, promoting the importance of a schoolwide approach to nutrition that involves everyone. School nutrition policies can focus on a commitment to good health by calling for healthy food choices throughout the school—in the classroom and cafeteria and at sports events and extra-curricular activities.

- *Parent and community involvement* can play a key role in fostering respect for and promotion of the health of others. When parents and community representatives are directly and frequently involved in the comprehensive school health system, they are acknowledging the value and importance of school health efforts for all children. The school can and should reach out to parents and community members, encouraging them to be presenters, volunteers, helpers, planners, or participants in events and activities in and outside of the classroom. Workshops for parents or visits to the home by school-linked providers of services may help communicate the importance and attributes of a supportive home environment in which students have positive role models and nurturing families.

Understanding Growth and Development

- A key aspect of *physical education* is an understanding of the process of human growth and development, including ways in which a combination of

Health-literate individuals understand and acknowledge the aspects of physical, mental, emotional, and social growth and development common to all people as well as those aspects that are unique to individuals.

163

Health-literate individuals select and use available health-related information, products, and services carefully and wisely.

proper diet and activity can contribute to lifelong health and prevention of disease. Also emphasized is the reality that individuals grow and develop at different rates yet in many ways are similar.

- *Psychological and counseling services* can help students and their families accept and understand numerous aspects of their own growth and development, including disabilities. Individual and group counseling can enhance students' self-esteem and minimize the self-doubt that often affects students in adolescence.

- *A safe and healthy school environment* acknowledges physical differences among students. For example, toilets, sinks, and drinking fountains are placed closer to the ground in areas used by younger students; all types of facilities are made accessible to those in wheelchairs; and emergency warning systems include a means of notifying deaf students and blind students.

Using Health-related Information, Products, and Services

- The school's *nutrition services* program can help prepare students to become well-informed consumers of healthy foods. The program can emphasize healthy foods in the daily menu and healthy food choices in the school cafeteria that extend to their ability to make well-informed decisions about food at home, in grocery stores and supermarkets, and in a variety of restaurants. It can also encourage students to be aware of the nutrient values of the foods they eat and information found on the labels of packaged foods.

- An awareness of health-related products, information, and services can be encouraged as part of the *safe and healthy school environment* component through efforts to inform students about aspects of the school environment that are health-promoting and those that need improvement. The school should use only nonpolluting, nontoxic chemicals and paints, for example, in cleaning and maintaining the physical plant. In many schools asbestos removal programs and other efforts to rid the environment of unhealthy chemicals or materials can be emphasized in health education. Less obvious environmental factors, such as building design, lighting, and sound deflection, can also be incorporated. Students can be involved in cleaning, maintaining, and enhancing the school building and grounds (for example, by planting trees and gardening) as one way of improving the school's physical plant and human climate.

- *Parent and community involvement* can play a critical role in making students aware of health-related resources in the community and of negative elements (for example, alcohol, tobacco, and other drugs or safety hazards) that might be a threat to children's health. An important emphasis in parent and community involvement can be to make students and their families aware of community services and resources available for assistance in emergencies and other health-care and support needs. Both formal resources (e.g., county agencies, community health-service providers) and informal resources (e.g., neighborhood groups, recreation clubs) should be featured.

- *Health promotion for staff* can and should encourage staff members themselves to be informed consum-

165

ers of goods and services that can affect their health. Staff members can, in turn, share this knowledge with students, thereby enhancing their position as healthy role models and health-literate adults.

In addition to promoting the four unifying ideas of health literacy in students, the components of a comprehensive school health system should be interrelated as much as possible. For example, specific organizing structures designed to advance health literacy schoolwide can be used. They may include frequent meetings of the school health committee and the coordinators of the eight components, such as teachers, nutrition services staff, nurses, school maintenance personnel, support staff, and parent and community volunteers. Another approach might be regular communication about the comprehensive school health system within the school. Staff meetings can emphasize ways in which the components of the comprehensive health system complement and support each other. Bulletins, in-service events, and other communications can emphasize health-related activities. Events such as health fairs and health career days can further convey the priority of health at the school and the many different ways in which the school develops and supports health literacy.

Also important in linking the components and developing a unified, coherent approach to a comprehensive school health system is continual emphasis on the conceptual and content linkages among the components. For example, all the components can support and relate to various aspects of *health education*. Activities can be arranged and coordinated so that special events developed by *nutrition services* support the study of foods and nutrients in the classroom. And students' testing of respiratory rates and physical fitness in *physical education* can be coordinated with the study of human growth and development.

Uniting the School, the Family, and the Community

A high degree of parent and community involvement is essential to unifying and strengthening the components of a comprehensive school health system. Parent and community involvement should be encouraged from the earliest stages of program planning and conceptualization and should be cultivated as programs continue and expand.

Parents, other family members, and representatives of the community, including representatives of community agencies and organizations that provide health-related services, can be linked to the comprehensive school health system in a variety of ways:

- Through emphasis on early identification of health problems, such as difficulties in seeing and hearing, recurrent infections, or chronic conditions, such as asthma, *health services* can promote parent and community involvement, underscoring the fact that everyone in the school and community has a role to play in maintaining the health of each child, no matter what the child's needs might be.

- In some cases students needing *psychological and counseling services* may have needs that cannot be met by the school's staff. Parents can then be referred to a variety of resources in the community.

- The *physical education* program can encourage students, their families, and staff members to take part in physical activity outside the school. Health clubs, sports leagues, programs sponsored by the local parks department or community-based organizations, family fun nights, organized hikes, and fund-raising walk-a-thons are all ways to show

Working with local parent-teacher groups, school nutrition personnel can introduce food-related issues, such as the importance of a good breakfast in promoting academic performance or information on how nutrition habits at home and after school affect choices at school .

support and enthusiasm for vigorous physical activity.

- The *nutrition services* program can help strengthen school-community linkages by disseminating information broadly about the school's nutrition services and community food and nutrition programs. For example, monthly lunch and breakfast menus can be printed with nutrition-related news for parents and students, such as healthy, easy-to-prepare recipes; and periodic updates can be provided to the school board, relevant governmental agencies, and the local media. Working with local parent-teacher groups, school nutrition personnel can introduce food-related issues, such as the importance of a good breakfast in promoting academic performance or information on how nutrition habits at home and after school affect choices at school. Good nutrition can also be promoted through collaboration with community groups and agencies, including professional associations interested in dietetics, medicine, child nutrition programs, and home economics and local community-based organizations that focus on youth and health issues. Connections with the food industry, including food producers, retail stores, and restaurants, are another way to promote the use of healthier food products throughout the community.

- The community can be involved in developing *health-promotion programs for school staff.* For example, local fitness centers may be able to offer group health-risk appraisals at reduced cost, and community health professionals can be invited to deliver informal noontime presentations on health to staff members.

- The community can also be involved in many different approaches to promoting a *safe and healthy school environment*. Above all, students should be encouraged to see the connections between all aspects of the environment, both in and out of school, and their own and others' health. Students should experience ways to give back to the community. For example, they can experience the satisfaction of helping others by visiting nursing homes, volunteering time at the local hospital, or collecting and distributing food for the homeless. Community service activities can be awarded credit toward graduation. Students can also be involved in community recycling programs. Students and teachers can organize ways to minimize air pollution from automobiles by coming to school in carpools or buses, on bicycles, or on foot. The school can communicate regularly about safety-related concerns with local emergency services agencies, law-enforcement agencies, fire-protection districts, and community-based organizations that can provide adults and students with training in such techniques as first aid and cardiopulmonary resuscitation (CPR).

Numerous other examples could be provided of effective ways to link the school, the family, and the community in health-related efforts. All can contribute to making the school and community an environment that promotes children's health. In addition, because in some cases the health of children can be improved only through direct services and support to families, the school-family-community linkages developed to support the comprehensive school health system can be used to provide school-linked services and support to families when needed.

Students should be encouraged to see the connections between all aspects of the environment, both in and out of school, and their own and others' health. Students should experience ways to give back to the community.

Building the
School Health Ship
and Setting Sail

An appropriate metaphor for the entire process of planning and implementing a comprehensive school health system is the analogy of building a ship and setting sail (see the following pages).

Essential to the ship's stability is health education. The ship's keel and ribs, which support the sheathing of the hull, are the nine different content areas. The four unifying ideas of health literacy connect the content areas and, with the content areas, form the hull.

However, health education and health-related information are only one element of a total approach to developing health literacy in children and youth.

The ship's sails, which catch the energy of motivation, direction, and purpose in the lives of individuals, institutions, and communities, are the seven other components of a comprehensive school health system.

Finally, the individual child, and ultimately every adult, is the captain of the ship, steering it in the direction of a healthy, successful life.

All those who plan and carry out components of the comprehensive school health system—in the school and in the community, as professionals, family members, or volunteers—can help to build a sound and sturdy ship for today's children and youths. When the ship is well designed and well constructed, it will be ready to weather the storms of life and take advantage of the gentle breezes that make life fulfilling.

170

Building the Hull of the Ship
(Knowledge, Attitudes, Behaviors)

Communicable and Chronic Diseases

Consumer and Community Health

Environmental Health

Family Living

Individual Growth and Development

Injury Prevention and Safety

Alcohol, Tobacco, and Other Drugs

Nutrition

Personal Health

Four Unifying Ideas of Health Literacy

- Acceptance of personal responsibility for lifelong health

- Respect for and promotion of the health of others

- An understanding of the process of growth and development

- Informed use of health-related information, products, and services

Set Your Sails
(Harnessing the Energy)

Health
Services

**Nutrition
Services**

Physical
Education

**Health Promotion
for Staff**

Parent and Community
Involvement

**Safe and Healthy School
Environment**

Counseling and
Psychological Services

Health Education

Chapter 5

Assessment of Health Literacy

Assessment approaches aligned with the desired expectations described in this framework are pivotal to the promotion of health literacy in children and youths. Since it is true that what is tested strongly influences what is taught, meaningful assessment focused on the knowledge, skills, attitudes, and behaviors necessary for health literacy should be built into curriculum design and the supporting structure from the outset.

Appropriate assessment will focus on the unifying ideas of health literacy. That is, it will attempt to measure students' progress toward:

- Accepting personal responsibility for lifelong health

- Respecting and promoting the health of others

- Understanding the process of growth and development

- Becoming informed users of health-related information, products, and services

The primary purpose of assessment should be to provide meaningful feedback to the student and teacher so that individual growth can be noted and future learning tailored to the student's needs.

The primary purpose of assessment should be to provide meaningful feedback to the student and teacher so that individual growth can be noted and future learning can be tailored to the student's needs. However, assessments in health education should be constructed to serve other important purposes. Because the health of students is influenced by the family, the community, the school, and peers, assessments should be designed to provide feedback to these groups. That is, assessment results should help parents, the community, and the students themselves understand the progress made toward health literacy for all students. These groups can use assessment results to help focus their efforts to support the development of health literacy and track progress over time.

Assessments also can provide valuable information for focusing and planning improvements in the comprehensive school health system.[1] Because student health literacy is best achieved when health education is provided within the context of a comprehensive school health system, effective assessment of health literacy must go beyond collecting only student-level data. Assessment should also examine the extent to which staff and the comprehensive school health system promote and reinforce health literacy. Such assessment results, together with

---

[1] See Chapter 1 for an explanation of the comprehensive school health system.

data from student assessments, can provide the information necessary to plan improvements in the comprehensive school health system. When implemented, these improvements can further promote the development of health literacy in all students. Assessments should:

- Be consistent with the unifying ideas of this framework.

- Focus on knowledge, skills, attitudes, and behaviors rather than on knowledge only.

- Provide useful feedback to individual students, teachers, and parents.

- Include the gathering of baseline health literacy data so that behavioral change can be tracked over time.

- Measure the extent to which the comprehensive school health system enhances and reinforces health literacy.

- Promote ongoing refinement of both health education and the entire comprehensive school health system.

ssessments should measure the extent to which the comprehensive school health system enhances and reinforces health literacy.

Student Assessment

In the planning of student assessment in health, the following principles underlying effective assessment should be considered and integrated into the assessment design:

- The assessment should examine the extent to which all students are achieving the four unifying ideas of health literacy.

- Rather than measuring knowledge only, the assessment should focus on health knowledge, healthy behaviors, attitudes about health, and skills to increase the prevalence of positive health behaviors and reduce the prevalence of negative health behaviors.

- The assessment should revolve around exemplary tasks aligned with this framework that provide information about student performance.

- The assessment tasks should be complex, open-ended, and meaningful. They should allow students to demonstrate thinking, understanding, and communication skills as well as mastery of health content. In contrast to traditional assessments, they should provide sufficient flexibility in approach so that students have opportunities to demonstrate health literacy in a variety of ways. An understanding should prevail that a variety of ways to solve a problem correctly may exist. Students should have ample time to work on assessment tasks and opportunities to revise and resubmit projects to raise performance to high-quality standards.

- Whenever possible, the assessment should be conducted in the course of normal work. The class and the learning should not, in most cases, be interrupted for a test.

- The primary purpose of the assessment should be to provide meaningful feedback to the student, parents, and teacher so that future learning can be tailored to the student's needs and parents can understand and support this learning.

Assessments based on these principles will include much more than the traditional methods of assessment, such as multiple choice, true-false, or machine-scored measures of acquired knowledge. A wide array of assessment methods and instruments that measure behavior and skill development and support critical thinking and a student-centered curriculum should be used to assess student health literacy. Examples of student assessments include:

- Using self-assessments that include a risk assessment or personal inventory to give students an understanding of their health status

- Using the results of a health-related physical fitness test to evaluate students' fitness level and to develop a personal fitness plan based on their level of fitness, knowledge acquired, and personal needs[2]

- Demonstrating an understanding of the connection between current behaviors and lifelong health by developing realistic and long-term goals related to health

- Role-playing ways to respond to physical, emotional, mental, and social changes that occur in a lifetime, including identifying available resources if needed

- Using positive social skills in small-group and large-group assignments with other students to work effectively toward a common goal

- Demonstrating specific decision-making, refusal, and conflict-resolution skills when given sample scenarios that allow students to grapple, in a safe environment, with difficult situations likely to happen during their lifetimes

- Reflecting, in journal entries, on the skills learned in the classroom and the use of those skills in the classroom, at school, with friends, or at home and indicating how those skills influence attitudes and behavior

A wide array of assessment methods and instruments which measure behavior and skill development and support critical thinking and a student-centered curriculum should be used to assess student health literacy.

---

[2] *Education Code* section 60608 requires school districts to administer a health-related physical fitness test to students in grades five, seven, and nine each year during March, April, or May.

- Recording food consumption in food diaries and using the diaries to analyze eating habits

- Developing a set of criteria for making decisions about health products that allow students to demonstrate an understanding of how marketing influences decision making

- Developing and using anonymous schoolwide surveys to obtain and analyze group data regarding negative and positive health behaviors, giving an important overall picture of the behavioral trends of students over time

- Developing and using student materials for schoolwide use that encourage actions and behaviors promoting good health, such as videos titled *Seat Belt, Skateboard, and Bicycle Safety* and *A Guide to Safe Dating* or a laminated poster illustrating emergency escape routes for each classroom

- Developing student portfolios that demonstrate the student's health literacy by addressing each of the four unifying ideas

One of the most effective ways to assess student progress toward health literacy is to observe whether their behavior supports or improves their health.

One of the most effective ways to assess student progress toward health literacy is to observe whether their behavior supports or improves their health. However, before assessments of behaviors are focused on, two cautionary notes are in order. First, what a student learns in health education may not produce observable behavioral changes until much later. To expect immediate change is unrealistic. Second, assessment of behavior must be carefully constructed to respect students' rights to privacy, community sensibilities, and existing laws and notification requirements. *Education Code* section 60650 requires parental permission to ask questions about the students' personal beliefs or practices and the parents' or guardians' beliefs and practices in the area of family living. Before any data on student behavior are collected, schools should consider working with parents and local community organizations or agencies to provide education and information about the assessment, the rationale for the assessment design, and the intended use of the assessment data. This communication with parents and the community can help prevent misunderstandings and garner support for quality assessments.

In addition to using assessment results with individual students, teachers should use student assessment data to evaluate the overall health curriculum. The data can provide insights as to whether the curriculum is meeting the needs of all students, is building on prior knowledge appropriately, and is consistent with the developmental levels of the students.

Voluntary assessments of staff health behaviors and attitudes about health will provide useful information about the staff's commitment to influencing students' health.

Staff Assessment

Because health education involves staff not only as teachers but as adult models of good health, the attitudes and habits of staff members regarding health play an important role in promoting student health literacy. Voluntary assessments of staff health behaviors and attitudes about health, as well as approaches used to promote health literacy, will provide useful information about the staff's commitment to influencing students' health and incorporating health literacy into their own lives. The results will serve as a needs assessment for designing professional development activities.

Whatever the grade level, staff assessment and follow-up staff development workshops should be based on current information about health literacy and effective teaching methods. Pedagogical skills that support critical thinking and a student-centered curriculum are required to address the unifying ideas and expectations of this framework. Assessment should focus on the extent to which teaching strategies support students in developing the knowledge, skills, attitudes, and behaviors necessary to achieve health literacy. For example, assessments might ask teachers to reflect on how their teaching strategies help students (1) develop decision-making and thinking skills; (2) solve problems individually and as part of a group inquiry; and (3) gather, analyze, and present information. Teachers might also reflect on how they support the development of student health literacy by (1) connecting concepts in health education with learning in other curriculum areas; (2) cooperating with other school staff members to make student health literacy a priority at the school; and (3) considering the culture, ethnic values, and customs of the community in curriculum design and delivery.

How instructional strategies used by teachers and the health literacy of teachers are assessed will depend on the resources and staff available. Assessment can be done through anonymous questionnaires, self-studies, or observations. One or more designated staff members, preferably members of the school or school district health committee, should take the lead and have the knowledge and skills needed to carry out this responsibility. The information collected will help staff reflect on their practices and determine changes they can make to promote student health literacy.

Assessment of the comprehensive school health system can provide invaluable information for planning program improvements to promote student health literacy.

System
Assessment

Assessment of the comprehensive school health system can provide invaluable information for planning program improvements to promote student health literacy. The assessment should involve both monitoring the implementation of a comprehensive school health system and evaluating the influence of this system on student health literacy. It should involve collecting data on such factors as the following:

- Number of students participating in different aspects of the comprehensive school health system, such as the number of students participating in planned, sequential health education and physical education

- Extent to which all the components of a comprehensive school health system are being implemented [3]

- Levels of parent and community involvement

- Degree to which appropriate program planning has taken place

- Extent to which the school vision for the comprehensive school health system has been articulated and the manner in which policies have been developed, reviewed, and implemented to support this vision

- Extent of linkages among the components of a comprehensive school health system

- Extent to which health education has been infused into the other curriculum areas

The assessment should also examine the allocation of staff and resources to support the comprehensive school health system. If available, community health data, such as the prevalence of iron-deficiency anemia among children, the number of accidents involving bicycles in the past year, the prevalence of sexually transmitted diseases among teenagers, or the incidence of teen pregnancy may be used together with school data. The assessment should be done in the initial planning stages and in each year thereafter so that schools can monitor their efforts to promote student health literacy and adjust those efforts as necessary to improve their effectiveness.

---

[3] See Chapter 1 for an explanation of the comprehensive school health system.

Using data from student, staff, and system assessments, the school should attempt to demonstrate, over a period of several years, the extent to which students have achieved health literacy and incorporated the values of that literacy into their daily living. Measuring the full continuum of outcomes, including positive changes in knowledge, attitudes, skills, and behaviors, will demand a variety of assessment methods and patience. Those planning assessments and using the assessment results must be mindful that change in behavior requires time. However, given the potential of assessment to influence long-term health behaviors of students, quality assessments must be developed and used to support progress toward health literacy for all students.

Chapter 6

Criteria for Evaluating Instructional Resources

The potential of this framework to influence classroom activities depends to a great extent on the quality of the instructional resources that support it. This chapter summarizes the criteria for the evaluation of health education instructional resources according to the philosophy, content, and guidelines presented in the previous chapters. Of particular importance is the contextual shift to teaching health within the context of a comprehensive school health system. In addition to the following criteria, the relevant portions of the California *Education Code* and the requirements of the *Standards for Evaluation of Instructional Materials with Respect to Social Content* should be noted.

The criteria, which address both content and pedagogy, are divided into the following categories:

- *Unifying Ideas*—which ideas and subject matter provide the basis for the instructional program

- *Accurate Content*—what is expected as to accuracy

- *Depth of Coverage*—what is expected as to depth of coverage in this thinking, meaning-centered curriculum

- *The Work Students Do*—what the students work on and how they do their work

- *Accessibility*—how the resources are presented and how the program deals with the diverse student population and the interests of students

- *Support for the Teacher*—how the resources support what the teacher does in the classroom

- *Assessment*—how the resources support assessment that is authentic, continual, student-interactive, and multifaceted

Each category offers a different perspective on how the total program is intended to be experienced by the students. The "Unifying Ideas," "Accurate Content," and "Depth of Coverage" criteria all primarily address issues related to content; the "Accessibility," "Support for the Teacher," and "Assessment" criteria primarily address pedagogy; and the criterion titled "The Work Students Do" addresses both content and pedogogical issues. In using these categories, reviewers should keep in mind the following general points:

- These categories are not distinct; they overlap. For example, students' experiences in a program cannot be accurately judged simply by looking at the category titled "The Work Students Do." Their experiences will also be affected by the quality of the teaching, the kinds of units and tasks worked on, and the content of the program.

- In each category all of the components of an instructional program (such as student materials, teacher materials, and technology) are to be examined as to how well they work together to provide a quality program for students in a classroom. These criteria do not presuppose the presence or absence of a particular component. It is possible to design a complete program that does *not* have a single student textbook and a high-quality program that has a student textbook at its center. Similarly, videotapes, computer software, and other technology might or might not be included in a program.

- Within each category is a series of subpoints that do not have to be of equal weight and should not be judged individually. Instead, they should be used to help identify the qualities that contribute to a category.

- Reviewers using these criteria must carefully evaluate how effective the instructional resources will be in the classroom. The resources need to be descriptive enough to help conscientious teachers implement a program that is aligned with this framework and yet is not so tightly structured that teachers have little flexibility.

Unifying Ideas

Instructional resources must reflect and support the unifying ideas and grade-level expectations of the framework. All of the unifying ideas, grade-level expectations, and nine content areas should be dealt with specifically over the course of a year. Overall, the units of instruction should interweave ideas from more than one of the nine content areas, and connections among the nine content areas should be made explicit within and among units. In addition, the resources must emphasize the mental and emotional aspects of health.

Health education should be taught in a comprehensive manner, its goal being the development of positive, life-long health behaviors and attitudes, and should be provided within the context of a comprehensive school health system. Resources should include opportunities to connect the classroom with school and community health-promotion activities. Skills and knowledge taught in the early grades should be reinforced and built on in the later grades.

Accurate Content

The content of the instructional resources must be based on scientific information, and clear references to current research on which the information is based should be included. Whenever possible, content should be presented confidently and not qualified with modifiers (such as "many researchers believe") when scientific generalizations are being discussed. Graphs, charts, tables, illustrations, and technology-based resources must be current and must be expressed in ways that are relevant to students' experiences. They also must support the unifying ideas and content of the framework.

Instructional resources should provide students with opportunities to evaluate the accuracy of health information with scientific criteria. As students explore, for example, the unifying idea titled "Informed Use of Health-related Information, Products, and Services," they should have opportunities to review critically their perceptions about health practices, health claims, and factors that influence the selection of products and services. Students should be asked to develop and apply criteria to distinguish products and services that are necessary, those that are not, and those that may be harmful.

Depth of Coverage

Instructional resources should emphasize depth of understanding, not breadth of coverage; they should not be encyclopedic. No single source can cover the entire discipline and do it well. Instead, instructional resources should take each unifying ideas and one or more of the content areas studied and interweave them in a logical, coherent manner. Clearly, a thematic orientation requires shortening or eliminating some material found in some instructional programs. However, the four unifying ideas should be included within each year.

Instructional resources should make connections with the components of a comprehensive school health system and with other academic disciplines when the connections enhance student learning and skill development in health. For example, literature connections can emphasize healthy behaviors and the impact of those behaviors on the individual, his or her family, and society.

Instructional resources must comply with current *Education Code* mandates. For example, resources that include a family life/sex education component must comply with *Education Code* sections 51550 and 51553 regarding sex education classes. And resources for students in grades seven through twelve must comply with *Education Code* sections 51201.5 and 51229.8 regarding HIV/AIDS education.

The Work Students Do

Instructional resources should encourage active learning on the part of students as they explore the unifying ideas and content areas described in Chapter 3. Student work should be active, meaningful, and integrative and should be connected to experience instead of being based on recall of information. Hands-on experiences are particularly important for students from diverse backgrounds. Activities should focus on the unifying ideas and the goal of developing positive, lifelong health behaviors; help students develop the skills described in Chapter 3; and support the unifying ideas and the grade-level expectations inside and outside of the classroom. Student work should involve the other elements of the comprehensive school health system within the school, the home, and the community.

Instructional resources should provide all students with opportunities for participation, recognition, and successful achievement, thereby fostering self-confidence and self-acceptance. Students, including those who have engaged in risk-taking behaviors, should have multiple opportunities to learn and practice skills involving decision making, refusal, problem solving, critical thinking, communication, self-improvement, coping, and stress reduction.

Students should encounter a varied program involving assignments that require complete student work. They should be asked to think, communicate, solve problems, and make positive, healthy decisions; formulate health questions; choose approaches to take; reflect frequently on the work they are doing; and make connections among ideas. Many tasks should require time and deliberation and be continued over several days. For extended assignments instructional resources should help teachers set clear criteria for student work and suggest ways to help students meet the criteria; but the resources should emphasize reasoning, not drill. Certain practices have been shown to discourage students and distance them from school, including excessive drill and practice and pressure to get a single correct answer on a recall test. Programs that allow for reflective thinking value a student's reasoning more than programs that consistently call for such an answer. This approach should be encouraged in whole-class, small-group, and independent work.

Instructional resources should call for students to interact with one another frequently. Heterogeneous, cooperative groups can explore the unifying ideas, the grade-level expectations, the nine content areas, and the health-related issues in depth and can help students of varied language backgrounds and achievement levels who are working toward a common instructional goal. Among the options for student-centered activities with language-minority students are grouping by language dominance, by English-language proficiency, and by mixed language, with some students playing the role of bilingual workers. Students should have frequent opportunities to practice the skills described in Chapter 3 and to communicate their findings by word of mouth, in writing, or through the use of multiple media. Students should be frequently asked to present their work to other audiences, including members of their families and communities.

Instructional resources should direct students to use technology-based resources to explore the unifying ideas and content described in Chapter 3. Interactive experiences involving technology can provide students with opportunities to practice skills as described in Chapter 3, reflect on consequences, interact with new information and reconfigure it, create products that demonstrate application of the concepts learned, and interact with other students and appropriate resource people outside the classroom. Students should be encouraged to seek supplementary resources and create their own through such means as surveys, studies, projects, case studies, or campaigns. Literature, reading lists, bibliographies, technology-based resources, community-resource directories, supplemental

189

activities, and chapter reviews should also be developed with those criteria in mind.

Instructional resources should link the classroom to the home and community through appropriate activities. In addition, the role of the family in the development and implementation of the comprehensive school health system, including school-linked services, should be reinforced. Finally, the influence of family, community, cultural background, language, the media, and peers should be made an integral part of the content and the instructional strategies.

Accessibility

The accessibility criterion contains two sections: (1) student diversity; and (2) presentation.

Student Diversity

Instructional resources must recognize cultural diversity and reflect strategies that research and practice have shown to be successful in engaging all students in learning. The resources should allow all students to participate fully in each unit, and the tasks and problems included should be accessible to all students. Woven throughout should be a multicultural perspective that respects the dignity and worth of all people regardless of their differences and builds on the knowledge, attitudes, beliefs, and cultural and linguistic foundation that students bring to class. The problems should be varied and open and should make investigation possible at many different levels. Units should allow students to go more deeply into some aspect of the unit's investigations according to their interests or their rapid grasp of the ideas. Activities or additional resources provided for students having difficulty should be in addition to, not instead of, the regular program.

The instructional resources should include activities that provide all students, including students with disabilities, with a common experiential base. Many tasks or lessons should use students' personal, family, or cultural experiences or other real-life contexts to create the specific content for the lesson. Students' beliefs about health, including cultural variations, should be considered and respected as a starting point in the development of healthy attitudes and behaviors.

Students with limited proficiency in English must not be excluded from the study of health until they are proficient in English. Therefore, teachers' editions and reference resources must provide ways in which instruction for limited-English-proficient (LEP) students can be made comprehensible and appropriate according to age and academic background. Providing materials in the primary languages of LEP students is one way of giving them access to the curriculum. Another is to provide glossaries; summaries of key concepts; and directions, instructions, or problems and tasks in the students' primary languages. In addition, formatting materials with clear headings, subheadings, illustrations, photographs, graphs, and charts all clearly labeled can greatly increase the likelihood that all students will understand basic concepts. Such conventions are crucial for special needs students, such as youngsters in the process of developing competency in English. The five largest language groups among LEP students in California that should be accommodated with resources are (in rank order) Spanish, Vietnamese, Cantonese, Hmong, and Cambodian.

The instructional resources should provide teachers with general and lesson-specific advice to support the learning of all students, including ways to:

- Bring the students' environment and daily experiences into the classroom to connect them in meaningful ways with the classroom activities.

191

- Encourage students to recognize and value the points of view and experiences of others where appropriate.

- Use peer support and collaborative learning groups.

- Work with students whose primary language is not English. Introduce techniques for using the primary language, sheltering the presentation, and incorporating technology-based resources so that these students' program is not limited or diluted.

- Deal with aspects of lessons that might generate conflicting feelings or responses from students and suggestions that promote teachers' sensitivity and respect for each student.

- Encourage students with disabilities to participate fully in the curriculum.

Presentation

The prose style of the instructional resources should be lively and engaging. Accordingly, vocabulary should be used to enhance student understanding but should not be allowed to dominate the purpose of learning, even for students learning English. Resources that contain an inordinate number of vocabulary lists and exercises may be intended more to define the words than to explain them and relate the concepts to which the words are germane. The resources should emphasize vocabulary development only when the terms introduced help students understand key concepts and communicate about the subject. Entries in glossaries should provide accurate examples and definitions and should differ from the treatment of vocabulary in the text. Because the best way to learn vocabulary is in the context of meaningful, interesting readings and activities, vocabulary development should not be isolated as an abstract intellectual exercise.

The resources should emphasize the positive nature of health literacy and the pleasure of a healthy life-style. They must link classroom health education and those social norms that support positive health behaviors with the student's own understanding of health.

Support for the Teacher

Instructional resources should provide many suggestions specific to lessons and units as well as illustrative examples of how the teacher can facilitate the student behaviors identified under "The Work Students Do." Suggestions for the teacher should be based on current research on learning styles and effective instruction. The resources should consistently include descriptions of the important health ideas within the units; suggestions for when in the curriculum information should be presented to students; descriptions of what units should look like when implemented in the classroom; and descriptions of how the experiences within units are related to what is known about the children's learning or developmental level. The resources should also provide information on what is important to do and say in a lesson or unit, suggested questions to ask, and ways to respond that encourage students to think about health and their health-related behaviors.

Materials should deal with suggestions for working with a diverse classroom of students, helping students work together productively, and managing technology-based resources so that the resources are accessible when students need to use them. Support for the teacher should also include ways to bring the student's environment and daily experi-

193

ence into the classroom so that the students connect effectively with classroom activities. The more relevant the knowledge and processes are to the students' everyday lives, the more likely they will be able to learn.

Teacher materials should also deal with ways to incorporate health education into the school's daily, weekly, and yearly schedule and connect health concepts with physical education and other areas of the curriculum.

Support for the teacher in carrying out assessment should include models for assessing student performance, using assessment results, and helping students assess their own health-related behavior. Resources can assist teachers in assessing their own health behaviors for modeling and can also suggest ways to involve teachers and other staff in conducting an assessment of the comprehensive school health system and using the results of the assessment when planning improvements.

Instructional resources should also contain ideas for linking the classroom to the comprehensive school health system. For example, resources might include suggestions for involving parents, keeping them informed about the program, and helping them access school-linked services. Suggestions might also include ways to create a positive classroom and school environment that supports a comprehensive school health system and acknowledges the parent's role in creating that environment. Materials should acknowledge that connections between the classroom and the community should be done in a manner consistent with policy adopted by the school district governing board. References to using guest or expert speakers from the community should also acknowledge that the speakers should be selected and involved in a manner consistent with board policy.

Assessment should be integrative and should be consistently aligned

Assessment

with the instructional program described in Chapter 5. The instructional resources should help teachers use a variety of assessment methods to get information about what the student or groups of students understand and are able to do in health education. Instructional resources must comply with current *Education Code* mandates regarding assessment, including Section 60650. Assessment of student progress should include measures not only of knowledge gained but also of skills learned and healthy behaviors commonly used. They should be designed to allow students access to technology-based resources or other resources, such as notes or reference documents, during the course of the assessment. Students should have ample time to work on assessment tasks and should have frequent opportunities to revise and resubmit projects to raise performance to high-quality standards.

Examination of student writing can be especially helpful in providing insights into health-related knowledge and development. Projects and essays can integrate writing skills and language arts concepts with the health curriculum. Students should be encouraged to assemble portfolios of their work in health education, including class exercises, teamwork, reports on activities, and creative projects.

By varying the format of assessment and collecting assessment data from multiple sources, teachers can better assess and appreciate the development of each student. They can then plan more effectively how to help students learn.

Chapter 7

Integration with Other Disciplines

The influence of well-planned, sequential health education can be enhanced through integration with other academic disciplines and components of a comprehensive school health system. Quality health education will take advantage of natural opportunities to achieve integration in as many ways as possible.

Effective integration does enhance student learning. However, the rigor of the individual disciplines must be maintained. Curriculum developers must plan meaningful integration while they are designing the curriculum so that integration can occur at the highest levels. Integrated activities must be preceded by careful planning. Certainly, integration must not be given as the reason for supplanting well-planned, sequential health education. The rest of this chapter presents ways in which health education can be integrated with the major areas of the curriculum. (See Figure 2 on page 206 for a sample plan for integrating a health concept.)

Language Arts

As students focus on an integrated curriculum in which reading, writing, speaking, and listening are treated together in meaningful contexts rather than apart from context, many opportunities exist for integrating language arts with health education. Literature frequently addresses basic health topics, such as how people interact, make personal choices, resolve conflicts, raise families, and function in a society in which alcohol, tobacco, and other drugs are widely used. One of the strongest ties between literature and health is support for the development of resiliency in children. Recognizing the resiliency that a character in literature must have to overcome conflicts or other difficult circumstances helps students learn how they too can become resilient, strong, healthy individuals.

The study of health provides writing opportunities across the curriculum. Journals may be kept on a variety of health issues, such as stress that causes anger and positive methods for controlling anger. Another might be students' reactions to advertisements for food or over-the-counter drugs. Students may be asked to write stories about how they envision their lives at ages twenty-one, forty-five, and sixty-five or to write on the topic What Is Unique About Me? Or they may be asked to write research papers on health topics, such as the effects of alcohol, tobacco, or other drugs on the body.

Oral-language development and reading skills can be improved through reading and discussing health-related literature. For example, at the upper elementary level, the reading of *Island of the Blue Dolphins* can lead to discussions about how members of a society and family support one another, what rationale exists for roles performed by members of a society, and how those roles may need to be modified as society changes. Literature allows students to experience the negative consequences of poor health choices in a risk-free way. High school students might read *Days of Wine and Roses* or other appropriate novels, for example, and then discuss the phenomenon of codependency and its short-range and long-range consequences without experiencing those consequences directly.

Oral-language development and reading skills can be improved through reading and discussing health-related literature.

History–Social Science

Numerous ties exist between the goals for history–social science and many health issues. In-depth examination of a culture or a period of history can address health issues, such as the availability of food and methods of food preparation, the structure and role of families, the impact of disease, the value placed on physical fitness, the relationships of individuals, and the influence of religious beliefs on society, especially as related to such health education issues as food choices and the use of alcohol, tobacco, or other drugs.

The history–social science strand of ethical and cultural literacy encourages students to develop a multicultural perspective that respects the dignity and worth of all people, providing opportunities to enrich and extend lessons supporting the unifying idea of respect and concern for the health of others.

Similarly, the history–social science goal of knowledge and cultural understanding lends itself to integration with health concepts. As students develop historical empathy and begin to analyze cause and effect, they can think about the pervasive effects that the personal health of our nation's leaders have had throughout history. Abraham Lincoln, for example, suffered from a genetic disorder, Marfan's syndrome, that isolated him as a child. He coped with it through his famous self-deprecating sense of humor. If Lincoln had been born "normal," would he have become President? The study of history and geography will sometimes include descriptions of the effects of natural disasters and the responses to such emergencies. In California the pattern of natural disasters from wildfires to earthquakes and the laws passed to protect the public from future occurrences might be included.

The history–social science strand of ethical and cultural literacy encourages students to develop a multicultural perspective that respects the dignity and worth of all people, providing opportunities to enrich and extend lessons supporting the unifying idea of respect and concern for the health of others. Environmental health issues, such as the effects of pesticides on the food chain, and public health laws can be examined as students explore economic and sociopolitical literacy.

A focus on democratic understanding and civic values can be linked to environmental health issues and the need to support the promotion of a safe and caring school environment. Students might, for example, study the founding of the Federal Drug Administration, the requirement for mass vaccinations, the creation of the National School Lunch Program, laws related to water purification, or the development of school policies related to a comprehensive school health system. The role of civic responsibility in environmental health as it relates to the development of laws, regulations, and advocacy can also be included. Studying America as a pluralistic and multicultural society presents opportunities for linking history–social science and family living. Students might, for example, do research and write an essay comparing intergenerational relationships in China with those in the United States.

The history–social science goal of skills attainment and social participation directly connect to many of the concepts and skills in health education. For example, effective personal skills, group-interaction skills, and social-participation skills are necessary to develop civic competence and positive health behaviors.

Science

As students explore science, health concepts can be used to link science with student experiences through hands-on exploration. For example, activities related to personal health, communicable and chronic diseases, nutrition, and the use of alcohol, tobacco, and other drugs can be developed to draw students into various aspects of life science. The study of food as an energy source can link physical sciences to student experiences in health. And students' interests in the study of geology and natural resources can be captured through the exploration of such environmental health issues as water use; waste disposal; and exposure to toxins, agricultural sprays, or smog.

The scientific process can be applied to many health-related problems of interest to students. While focusing on the unifying idea of personal responsibility, students can grow cultures with materials scraped from under their fingernails or from their teeth. They can observe the growth of the cultures, write about what they see, and compare results. Further study of

The scientific process can be applied to many health-related problems of interest to students.

basic hygiene might lead students to relating good health practices, such as washing the hands, with the spread of disease. The study of environmental issues and their effects on health also provides many opportunities to apply scientific processes.

Mathematics

As students gain the ability to discern mathematical relationships, reason logically, and use mathematical techniques effectively, they will have many opportunities to link mathematical techniques with health problems that are open-ended and meaningful to students. For example, as elementary students focus on the unifying idea of the process of growth and development, they can graph the range of heights of class members and determine an average at the beginning and end of the term. Foods eaten by students can be analyzed as to the number of servings eaten from each of the food groups described in the *California Daily Food Guide* or as to nutrient composition. Determining how to share a snack with a table group, comparing how much different containers hold to find the best buy at the supermarket, and deciding how much food to purchase for a class celebration are all further examples of realistic activities in mathematics.

Older students can calculate the lifetime costs of smoking, both direct and indirect, to the individual and society and can calculate and graph health-care costs resulting from lung cancer. Activities related to the unifying idea of respect for and promotion of the health of others can be reinforced by having students research and calculate the costs of raising a child from birth through age twenty-one and considering future costs by analyzing trends in inflation.

Beyond computation the mathematics curriculum also includes the important strands of statistics and probability, patterns and functions, and logic. These skills can be applied to the study of disease control and to the development of the consumer skills needed to distinguish valid and invalid health claims.

Physical Education

Physical education offers an ideal opportunity for integrating into actual practice many of the concepts of health education. Schoolwide health and physical activity days or fairs can celebrate the benefits of personal health goals in a community context. In addition, effective use of protective gear during sports activities and the study of the connection between appropriate back exercises to strengthen stomach muscles and prevention of back injuries can support the theme of personal responsibility. Individual fitness programs in which students log their heart rates, weight, activity, and food choices weekly can be related to health units dealing with the unifying idea of personal responsibility.

Examining the use and dangers of such performance-enhancing drugs as steroids is an appropriate activity in both health education and physical education. Similarly, students can examine the links between physical activity, food intake, and body composition.

Visual and Performing Arts

The arts provide students with a unique way of exploring health-related issues. They offer risk-free exploration of the consequences of health-related choices.

The visual and performing arts provide students with opportunities to explore the expression of ideas, emotions, and beliefs through different media, such as painting, sculpture, architecture, dance, movement, music, dramatics, and theater. In expressing the creative power of their minds through the arts, students become cognizant of and value their own capacities and personal uniqueness as well as the creative expressions of others. They also study aesthetics, cultural heritage, and the history of the visual and performing arts, including the continuing influence of the arts on societies worldwide.

The arts provide students with a unique way of exploring health-related issues. They offer risk-free exploration of the consequences of health-related choices. For example, students can create and produce a play dramatizing the different ways in which two individuals—one with high self-esteem, the other with low self-esteem—cope with the temptations and pressures of high school life. Drama can also provide students with the opportunity to examine the resiliency that an individual must have to overcome conflict.

Songs and plays can demonstrate positive ways to celebrate without the use of alcohol, tobacco, or other drugs. In fact, they may be the only way to convey a "no-use" message to certain students. The students viewing the performances can reflect about what they have seen and heard in a way that cannot be provided through classroom instruction. The visual arts can also provide students with opportunities to communicate health concepts. For example, students can create posters about our multicultural society, friendship, or their own uniqueness.

Foreign Languages

Studying foreign languages also provides opportunities to strengthen students' understanding of health-related concepts. For example, personal health concerns are basic to learning a second language. The ability to communicate about such needs as how to obtain food, where to sleep, and how to obtain assistance when necessary is critical if students are to communicate effectively in another language.

The study of foreign languages also involves the investigation of another culture. Issues such as cultural food habits, unique family interactions, health beliefs and practices, and values about other health-related areas can be investigated. Exploring food-related customs by preparing a typical meal, discussing its nutritional quality, and conversing only in the target language while eating would be one way to involve students actively in another culture.

Once students have gained some proficiency in the target language, they can assist the school in its efforts to involve all parents in the comprehensive school health system. Preparation of emergency plans in languages other than English may be helpful to members of the community in an emergency. Students may also serve as translators for parents or other members of the community who need assistance.

Figure 2

Sample Plan for Integrating a Health Education Topic with Other Disciplines

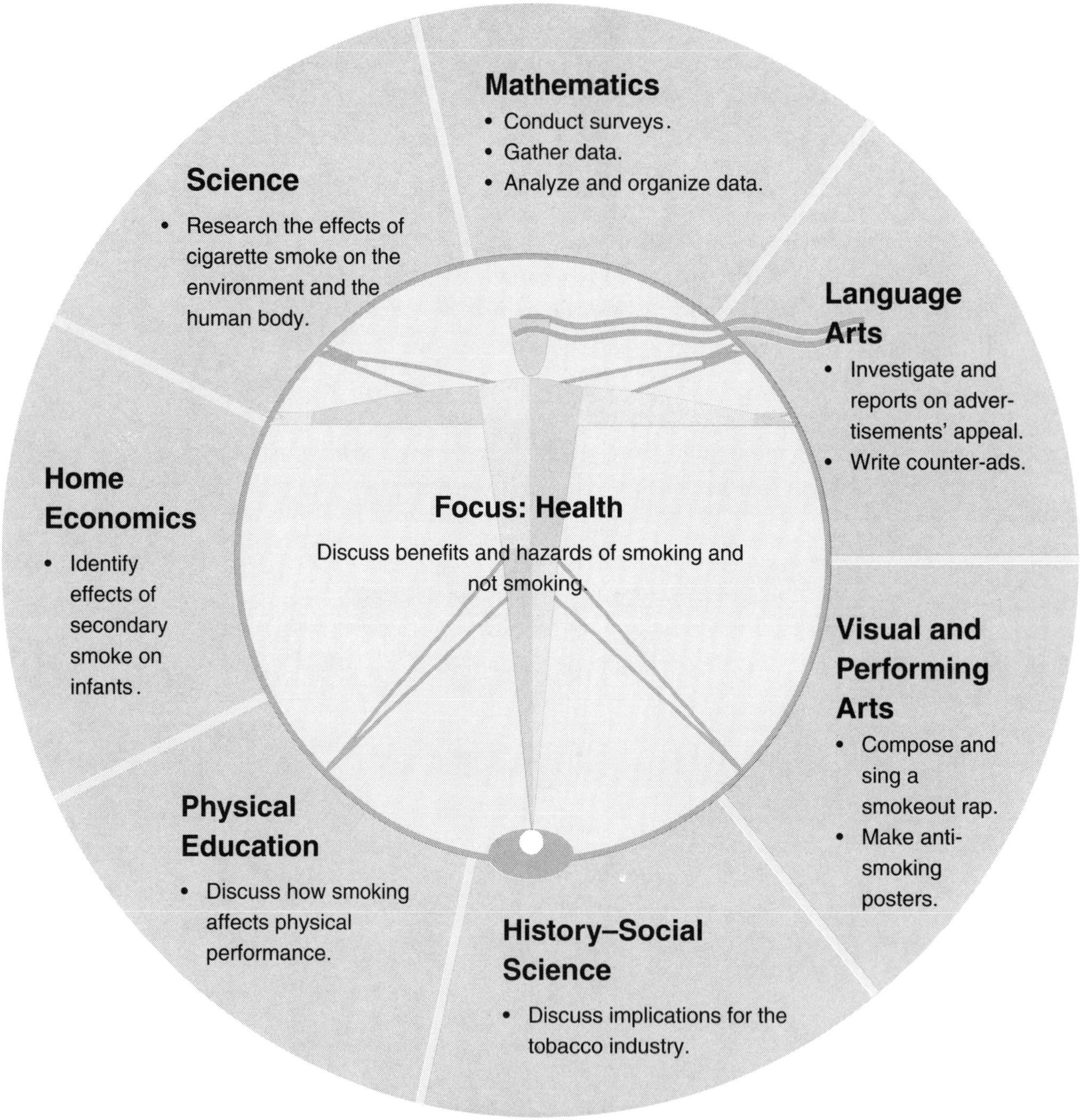

Mathematics
- Conduct surveys.
- Gather data.
- Analyze and organize data.

Science
- Research the effects of cigarette smoke on the environment and the human body.

Language Arts
- Investigate and reports on advertisements' appeal.
- Write counter-ads.

Home Economics
- Identify effects of secondary smoke on infants.

Focus: Health
Discuss benefits and hazards of smoking and not smoking.

Visual and Performing Arts
- Compose and sing a smokeout rap.
- Make anti-smoking posters.

Physical Education
- Discuss how smoking affects physical performance.

History–Social Science
- Discuss implications for the tobacco industry.

Adapted from J. M. Palmer, *Educational Leadership*, Vol. 49, No. 2 (1991).

Selected Education Code Sections

This appendix contains selected *Education Code* sections that may interest those involved in implementing this framework. The sections were current at the time of publication. However, those using this appendix should keep in mind that the code sections may be amended by subsequent legislation. Educators and others interested in supporting the comprehensive school health system are therefore encouraged to keep up to date on legislative changes affecting health and health education.

This appendix is divided into two sections, the first dealing specifically with instruction and the second with aspects of the comprehensive school health system. The code sections are listed in numerical order within each section.

Education Code Sections Pertinent to Instruction

8850.5. Family relationships and parenting education

"Family relationships and parenting education," as used in this chapter, means an instructional program designed to provide pupils at all grade levels with age-appropriate components, including all of the following:

(a) Development of an understanding of the physical, mental, emotional, social, economic, and psychological aspects of themselves and others, and of the physiological, psychological, and cultural foundations of human development.

(b) The opportunity to acquire knowledge which will support the development of responsible family relationships, strengthen the pupil's current family life, and further the understanding of the role of the parent.

(c) Development of an understanding of the consequences of decisions and actions upon personal, family, and peer relationships.

(d) Recognition of, and attention to, the significance of healthy self-esteem in the growth and development of healthy human beings.

44806. Duty concerning instruction of pupils concerning morals, manners, and citizenship

Each teacher shall endeavor to impress upon the minds of the pupils the principles of morality, truth, justice, patriotism, and a true comprehension of the rights, duties, and dignity of American citizenship, including kindness toward domestic pets and the humane treatment of living creatures, to teach them to avoid idleness, profanity, and falsehood, and to instruct them in manners and morals and the principles of a free government.

51201.5 Instruction on AIDS and AIDS prevention; information and recommendations

(a) Commencing in the 1992-93 school year, school districts shall ensure that all pupils in grades 7 to 12, inclusive, or the equivalent thereof, except as otherwise provided in subdivision (c), receive AIDS prevention instruction from adequately trained instructors in appropriate courses. Each pupil shall receive the instruction at least once in junior high or middle school and once in high school. For the purposes of this subdivision, "school district" includes county boards of education, county superintendents of schools, and the State Schools for the Handicapped.

(b) The required AIDS prevention instruction shall accurately reflect the latest information and recommendations from the United States Surgeon General, federal Centers for Disease Control, and the National Academy of Sciences, and shall include the following:

    (1) Information on the nature of AIDS and its effects on the human body.

    (2) Information on how the human immunodeficiency virus (HIV) is and is not transmitted, including information on activities that present the highest risk of HIV infection.

    (3) Discussion of methods to reduce the risk of HIV infection. This instruction shall emphasize that sexual abstinence and abstinence from intravenous drug use are the most effective means for AIDS prevention, but shall also include statistics based upon the latest medical information citing the failure and success rates of condoms and other contraceptives in preventing sexually transmitted HIV infection and information on other methods that may reduce the risk of HIV transmission from intravenous drug use. Nothing in this section shall be construed to supersede Section 51533.

    (4) Discussion of the public health issues associated with AIDS.

    (5) Information on local resources for HIV testing and medical care.

    (6) Development of refusal skills to assist pupils to overcome peer pressure and use effective decision-making skills to avoid high-risk activities.

    (7) Discussion about societal views on AIDS, including stereotypes and myths regarding persons with AIDS. This instruction shall emphasize compassion for persons with AIDS.

(c) The governing board of each school district, each county board of education, and each county superintendent of schools, as applicable, shall provide the parent or guardian of each pupil in grades 7 to 12, inclusive, or the equivalent thereof, with written notice explaining the purpose of the AIDS prevention instruction. The Superintendent of Public Instruction shall provide the parent or guardian of each pupil in grades 7 to 12, inclusive, or the equivalent thereof, in the State Schools for the Handicapped with written notice explaining the purpose of the AIDS prevention instruction. The notice shall specify that any parent or guardian may request that his or her child or ward not receive instruction in AIDS prevention. No pupil shall attend the AIDS prevention instruction if a written request that he or she not attend has been received by the school. For the governing boards of school districts, this notification shall accompany the reporting of rights and responsibilities required by Section 48980. If authorized by the school district governing board, a school district may require parental consent prior to providing instruction on AIDS prevention to any minor pupil.

(d) All school districts shall ensure all of the following:

  (1) That instructional materials related to this instruction are available.

  (2) That these instructional materials are appropriate for use with pupils of various ages and learning abilities.

  (3) That these instructional materials may be used effectively with pupils from a variety of ethnic, cultural, and linguistic backgrounds, and special needs.

51202. Instruction in personal and public health and safety

The adopted course of study shall provide instruction at the appropriate elementary and secondary grade levels and subject areas in personal and public safety and accident prevention, including emergency first aid instruction, instruction in hemorrhage control, treatment for poisoning, resuscitation techniques, and cardiopulmonary resuscitation when appropriate equipment is available; fire prevention; the protection and conservation of resources, including the necessity for the protection of our environment; and health, including venereal disease and the effects of alcohol, narcotics, drugs, and tobacco upon the human body. The health instruction may include prenatal care for pregnant women and violence as a public health issue.

51203. Instruction on alcohol, narcotics and restricted dangerous drugs

Instruction upon the nature of alcohol, narcotics, restricted dangerous drugs as defined in Section 11032 of the Health and Safety

Code, and other dangerous substances and their effects upon the human system as determined by science shall be included in the curriculum of all elementary and secondary schools. Instruction on the effects of alcohol, narcotics, restricted dangerous drugs as defined in Section 11032 of the Health and Safety Code, and other dangerous substances upon prenatal development as determined by science shall be included in the curriculum of all secondary schools. The governing board of the district shall adopt regulations specifying the grade or grades and the course or courses in which the instruction with respect to alcohol, narcotics, restricted dangerous drugs as defined in Section 11032 of the Health and Safety Code, and other dangerous substances shall be included. All persons responsible for the preparation or enforcement of courses of study shall provide for instruction on the subjects of alcohol, narcotics, restricted dangerous drugs as defined in Section 11032 of the Health and Safety Code, and other dangerous substances.

51210. Areas of study

The adopted course of study for grades 1 through 6 shall include instruction, beginning in grade 1 and continuing through grade 6, in the following areas of study:

(f)   Health, including instruction in the principles and practices of individual, family, and community health.

51220.5. Parenting skills; areas of instruction; community colleges

(a)   The Legislature finds and declares the following:

(1)   The family is our most fundamental social institution and the means by which we care for, prepare, and train our children to be productive members of society.

(2)   Social research shows increasingly that the disintegration of the family is a major cause of increased welfare enrollment, child abuse and neglect, juvenile delinquency, and criminal activity.

(3)   The lack of knowledge of parenting skills and the lack of adequate preparation to assume parental responsibilities are not only major causes of family disintegration, but also contribute substantially to the disastrous consequences of teen pregnancy.

(4)   Because the state government bears much of the economic and social burden associated with the disintegration of the family in California, the state has a legitimate and vital interest in adequately preparing its residents for parenthood.

(b)   The Legislature recognizes that the public education system is the most efficient and effective means to educate the populace on a large-scale basis, and intends, therefore, to use the public education system to ensure that each California resident has an opportunity to acquire knowledge of parenting skills prior to becoming a parent. That knowledge should include, at a bare minimum, all of the following:

(1)   Child development and growth.
(2)   Effective parenting.
(3)   Prevention of child abuse.
(4)   Nutrition.
(5)   Household finances and budgeting.
(6)   Personal and family interaction and relations.
(7)   Methods to promote self-esteem.
(8)   Effective decisionmaking skills.
(9)   Family and individual health.

(c)   Commencing with the 1994-95 fiscal year, the adopted course of study for grade 7 or 8 shall include the equivalent content of a one-semester course in parenting skills and education. All pupils entering grade 7 on or after July 1, 1994, shall be offered that course or its equivalent content during grade 7 or 8, or both. On or before September 1, 1993, the State Department of Education shall supply, to each school district that includes a grade 7 or 8, a sample curriculum suitable either for implementation as a stand-alone one-semester course or for incorporation within identified existing required or optional courses, with content designed to develop a knowledge of topics including, but not limited to, all of the following:

(1)   Child growth and development.
(2)   Parental responsibilities.
(3)   Household budgeting.
(4)   Child abuse and neglect issues.
(5)   Personal hygiene.
(6)   Maintaining healthy relationships.
(7)   Teen parenting issues.
(8)   Self-esteem.

(d)   Commencing with the 1993-94 fiscal year, community college districts may offer, to interested individuals, noncredit fee-supported courses in parenting skills and education as described in subdivision (c).

(e)   This section is not intended to replace existing courses that accomplish the intent of this section. School districts may meet the requirements of this section with existing courses of study offered in any of grades 6 to 9, inclusive, that includes the course contents identified in subdivision (c).

(f)   This section shall become operative only if a funding source is identified by the Superintendent of Public Instruction for the purposes of this section on or before January 1, 1995.

(g)   The Superintendent of Public Instruction shall identify the funding source for this section from existing resources or private resources, or both, that may be available for the purposes of this section. The superintendent shall notify school districts when sufficient funds have been identified and are allocated to cover all costs relating to the operation of Section 51220.5 of the Education Code.

51240. Excuse from health, family life, and sex education instruction due to religious beliefs

Whenever any part of the instruction in health, family life education, and sex education conflicts with the religious training and beliefs of the parent or guardian of any pupil, the pupil, on written request of the parent or guardian, shall be excused from the part of the training which conflicts with such religious training and beliefs.

As used in this section, "religious training and beliefs" includes personal moral convictions.

51260. Elementary and secondary school instruction by appropriately trained instructors; services to be nonduplicative

(a)   Instruction shall be given in the elementary and secondary schools by appropriately trained instructors on drug education and the effects of the use of tobacco, alcohol, narcotics, dangerous drugs, as defined in Section 11032 of the Health and Safety Code, and other dangerous substances.

For purposes of this chapter, an "appropriately trained instructor" is one who, based upon the determination of the site administrator, demonstrates competencies in interacting in a positive manner with children and youth; demonstrates knowledge of the properties and effects of tobacco, alcohol, narcotics, and dangerous drugs; and who demonstrates skills in conducting affective education, which include methods and techniques for helping children and youth to freely express ideas and opinions in a responsible manner and to gain an awareness of their values as they affect decisions related to drug use and misuse.

In grades 1 through 6, instruction on drug education should be conducted in conjunction with courses given on health pursuant to subdivision (f) of Section 51210.

In grades 7 to 12, inclusive, instruction on drug education shall be conducted in conjunction with courses given on health or in any appropriate area of study pursuant to Section 51220.

Such instruction shall be sequential in nature and suited to meet the needs of students at their respective grade level.

(b)   Services provided under this section shall be in addition to, but shall not be duplicative of, services provided pursuant to Article 2 (commencing with Section 11965) of Part 3 of Division 10.5 of the Health and Safety Code.

51262. Use of anabolic steroids; legislative finding and declaration; preparation and distribution of steroid education package

The Legislature hereby finds and declares that the use of anabolic steroids to expedite the physical development and to enhance the performance level of secondary school athletes presents a serious health hazard to these student athletes. It is the intent of the Legislature in enacting this measure that, beginning with the 1987-88 school year, schools be encouraged to include in instruction in grades 7 to 12, inclusive, in science, health, drug abuse, or physical education programs a lesson on the effects of the use of anabolic steriods.

In order to increase the knowledge of students about the effects of the use of anabolic steroids, the Superintendent of Public Instruction shall develop a steroid education package consisting of teacher lesson plans, student pamphlets, parent pamphlets, and video tapes to be distributed directly to school districts.

51265. Legislative intent; gang violence and drug and alcohol abuse prevention in-service training

It is the intent of the Legislature that school districts and county offices of education give high priority to gang violence and drug and alcohol abuse prevention in-service training programs, which shall be part of the overall strategy for comprehensive gang violence and drug and alcohol abuse prevention education.

"Gang violence and drug and alcohol abuse prevention in-service training" for purposes of this article means the presentation of programs, instruction and curricula that will help educators develop competencies in interacting in a positive manner with children and youth to assist them in developing the positive values, self-esteem, knowledge, and skills to lead productive, gang-free and drug-free lives; develop knowledge of the causes of gang violence and substance abuse, and the properties and effects of tobacco, alcohol, narcotics, and dangerous drugs, including the risk of contracting acquired immune deficiency syndrome (AIDS) associated with intravenous drug use; receive training regarding available information and resources concerning gang violence and drug and alcohol abuse prevention as well as antigang and antisubstance abuse crime trends; develop familiarity with teaching social skills and resistance skills to children and youth; and develop skills in conducting effective education, which includes methods and techniques for helping children and youth to freely express ideas and opinions in a responsible manner and to understand the nature and consequences of their decisions as they relate to gang involvement and drug and alcohol abuse.

51550. Sex education courses

No governing board of a public elementary or secondary school may require pupils to attend any class in which human reproductive organs and their functions and processes are described, illustrated or discussed, whether such class be part of a course designated "sex education" or "family life education" or by some similar term, or part of any other course which pupils are required to attend.

If classes are offered in public elementary and secondary schools in which human reproductive organs and their functions and processes are described, illustrated or discussed, the parent or guardian of each pupil enrolled in such class shall first be notified in writing of the class. Sending the required notice through the regular United States mail, or any other method which such local school district commonly uses to communicate individually in writing to all parents, meets the notification requirements of this paragraph.

Opportunity shall be provided to each parent or guardian to request in writing that his child not attend the class. Such requests shall be valid for the school year in which they are submitted but may be withdrawn by the parent or guardian at any time. No child may attend a class if a request that he not attend the class has been received by the school.

Any written or audiovisual material to be used in a class in which human reproductive organs and their functions and processes are described, illustrated, or discussed shall be available for inspection by the parent or guardian at reasonable times and places prior to the holding of a course which includes such classes. The parent or guardian shall be notified in writing of his opportunity to inspect and review such materials.

This section shall not apply to description or illustration of human reproductive organs which may appear in a textbook, adopted pursuant to law, on physiology, biology, zoology, general science, personal hygiene, or health.

Nothing in this section shall be construed as encouraging the description, illustration, or discussion of human reproductive organs and their functions and processes in the public elementary and secondary schools.

The certification document of any person charged with the responsibility of making any instructional material available for inspection under this section or who is charged with the responsibility of notifying a parent or guardian of any class conducted within the purview of this section, and who knowingly and willfully fails to make such instructional material available for inspection or to notify such parent or guardian, may be revoked or suspended because of such act. The certification document of any person who knowingly and willfully requires a pupil to attend a class within the purview of this section when a request that the pupil not attend has been received from the parent or guardian may be revoked or suspended because of such act.

51553. Sex education classes; course criteria

(a) All public elementary, junior high, and senior high school classes that teach sex education and discuss sexual intercourse shall emphasize that abstinence from sexual intercourse is the only protection that is 100 percent effective against unwanted teenage pregnancy, sexually transmitted diseases, and acquired immune deficiency syndrome (AIDS) when transmitted sexually. All material and instruction in classes that teach sex education and discuss sexual intercourse shall be age appropriate.

(b) All sex education courses that discuss sexual intercourse shall satisfy the following criteria:

  (1) Course material and instruction shall be age appropriate.

  (2) Course material and instruction shall stress that abstinence is the only contraceptive method which is 100 percent effective, and that all other methods of contraception carry a risk of failure in preventing unwanted teenage pregnancy. Statistics based on the latest medical information shall be provided to pupils citing the failure and success rates of condoms and other contraceptives in preventing pregnancy.

  (3) Course material and instruction shall stress that sexually transmitted diseases are serious possible hazards of

sexual intercourse. Pupils shall be provided with statistics based on the latest medical information citing the failure and success rates of condoms in preventing AIDS and other sexually transmitted diseases.

(4) Course material and instruction shall include a discussion of the possible emotional and psychological consequences of preadolescent and adolescent sexual intercourse outside of marriage and the consequences of unwanted adolescent pregnancy.

(5) Course material and instruction shall stress that pupils should abstain from sexual intercourse until they are ready for marriage.

(6) Course material and instruction shall teach honor and respect for monogamous heterosexual marriage.

(7) Course material and instruction shall advise pupils of the laws pertaining to their financial responsibility to children born in and out of wedlock.

(8) Course material and instruction shall advise pupils that it is unlawful for males of any age to have sexual relations with females under the age of 18 to whom they are not married pursuant to Section 261.5 of the Penal Code.

(9) Course material and instruction shall emphasize that the pupil has the power to control personal behavior. Pupils shall be encouraged to base their actions on reasoning, self-discipline, sense of responsibility, self-control, and ethical considerations, such as respect for one's self and others.

(10) Course material and instruction shall teach pupils to not make unwanted physical and verbal sexual advances and how to say no to unwanted sexual advances. Pupils shall be taught that it is wrong to take advantage of, or to exploit, another person. The material and instruction shall also encourage youth to resist negative peer pressure.

(c) This section shall become operative July 1, 1989.

51820. Venereal disease instruction; written notification to parent; inspection of instructional material; consensual pupil participation

The governing board of any district maintaining elementary or secondary schools may offer units of instruction in venereal disease education in such schools with the assistance and guidance of the State Department of Education. The grade level at which such instruction shall be given shall be determined by the governing board of the school district.

Nothing in this section shall be construed as prohibiting or limiting any right provided for in Section 51240.

If venereal disease education classes are offered, the parent or guardian of each pupil enrolled or to be enrolled therein shall be notified in writing of the instructional program. Such notice shall be given at least 15 days prior to the commencement of the instructional program. The notice shall also advise the parent or guardian of his right to inspect the instructional materials to be used in such class and of his right to request the school authorities that his child not attend any such class.

Sending the required notice through the regular United States mail or any other method of delivery which the school district commonly uses to communicate individually in writing to all parents, meets the notification requirements of this section.

The parent or guardian may request that his child not participate in a venereal disease instruction program. Such request shall be in writing, but may be withdrawn by the parent or guardian at any time. No pupil may attend any class in venereal disease education, if a request that he not attend the class has been received by the school in the manner provided in this section.

The parent or guardian of any pupil enrolled or to be enrolled in any venereal disease education class shall be provided the opportunity to inspect the textbooks, audiovisual aids, and any other instructional materials to be used in such classes.

60650. Personal Beliefs

No test, questionnaire, survey, or examination containing any questions about the pupil's personal beliefs or practices in sex, family life, morality and religion, or any questions about his parents', or guardians' beliefs and practices in sex, family life, morality and religion, shall be administered to any pupil in kindergarten or grade 1 through grade 12, inclusive, unless the parent or guardian of the pupil is notified in writing that such test, questionnaire, survey, or examination is to be administered and the parent or guardian of the pupil gives written permission for the pupil to take such test, questionnaire, survey, or examination.

Education Code Sections Pertinent to the Comprehensive School Health System

39876. Sale of specified food items

A minimum of 50 percent of the items, other then foods reimbursed under Chapters 13 (commencing with Section 1751) and 13A (commencing with Section 1771) of Title 42 of the United States Code, offered for sale each schoolday at any school site by any entity or organization during regular school hours shall be selected from the following list:

(a) Milk and dairy products, including cheese, yogurt, frozen yogurt, and ice cream.

(b) Full-strength fruit and vegetable juices and fruit drinks containing 50 percent or more full-strength fruit juice, and fruit nectars containing 35 percent or more full-strength fruit juice.

(c) Fresh, frozen, canned, and dried fruits and vegetables.

(d) Nuts, seeds, and nut butters.

(e) Nonconfection grain products, as defined by regulation of the United States Food and Drug Administration, including crackers, bread sticks, tortillas, pizza, pretzels, bagels, muffins, and popcorn.

(f) Meat, poultry, and fish, and their products, including beef jerky, tacos, meat turnovers, pizza, chili, and sandwiches.

(g) Legumes and legume products, including bean burritos, chili beans, bean dip, roasted soy beans, and soups.

(h) Any foods which would qualify as one of the required food components of the Type A lunch which is defined in and reimbursable under the National School Lunch Act (Ch. 13 (commencing with Section 1751), Title 42, U.S.C.).

For the purposes of this section, "item" shall be defined as each separate kind of food offered for sale as a separate unit.

48931. Authorization for sale of food by student or adult entity or organization

The governing board of any school district or any county office of education may authorize any pupil or adult entity or organization to sell food on school premises, subject to policy and regulations of the State Board of Education. The State Board of Education shall develop policy and regulations for the sale of food by any pupil or adult entity or organization, or any combination thereof, which shall ensure optimum participation in the school district's or the county office of education's nonprofit food service programs and shall be in consideration of all programs approved by the governing board of any school district or any county office of education. The policy and regulations shall be effective the first of the month following adoption by the State Board of Education.

Nothing in this section shall be construed as exempting from the California Uniform Retail Food Facilities Law (Chapter 4 (commencing with Section 27500) of Division 22 of the Health and Safety Code), food sales which are authorized pursuant to this section and which would otherwise be subject to the California Uniform Retail Food Facilities Law.

49490. Legislative findings and declarations

The Legislature finds and declares that hunger and malnutrition among children from low-income families constitute one of the most critical child health problems in the state; that federal programs to meet child nutrition needs are providing nourishing meals to thousands of the state's poverty area children who previously could not participate in school lunch programs; that federal funds allocated for child nutrition to California are inadequate to meet critical needs; that the state and local communities bear a responsibility towards meeting these needs; and that the physical well-being of all of the children of the state is a matter of public concern and expenditures to secure such well-being serves a public purpose.

49500. Meals for pupils

The governing board of any school district may provide, without charge or at a reduced price, breakfasts for pupils within the district who are needy. The governing board may provide, without charge or at a reduced price, lunches for pupils who are needy. The governing board of any school district may provide, without charge, lunches for any or all other pupils whether they are needy or not, provided that the governing board has so provided such lunches without charge to all pupils of the district during the 1962-1963 school year. The governing board of any school district may provide, without charge or at a reduced price, other nutrition periods during the schoolday during which foods or beverages, or both, are served to pupils.

For purposes of this article a pupil who is "needy" is one who does not otherwise receive proper nourishment.

As used in this article "school meals" includes breakfasts, lunches, or the serving of foods or beverages, or both, during other nutrition periods, or any combination thereof.

49530. Legislative intent

(a) The Legislature finds that (1) the proper nutrition of children is a matter of highest state priority, and (2) there is a demonstrated relationship between the intake of food and good nutrition and the capacity of children to develop and learn, and (3) the teaching of the principles of good nutrition in schools is urgently needed to assist children at all income levels in developing the proper eating habits essential for lifelong good health and productivity.

(b) It is the policy of the State of California that no child shall go hungry at school or a child development program and that schools and child development programs conducted pursuant to Chapter 2 (commencing with Section 8200) of Part 6 of Division 1 of Title 1 have an obligation to provide for the nutritional needs and nutrition education of all pupils during the schoolday and all children receiving child development services.

51890. "Comprehensive health education programs"

For the purposes of this chapter, "comprehensive health education programs" are defined as all educational programs offered in kindergarten and grades 1 through 12, inclusive, in the public school system, including in-class and out-of-class activities designed to ensure that:

(a) Pupils will receive instruction to aid them in making decisions in matters of personal, family, and community health, to include the following subjects:

    (1) The use of health care services and products.

    (2) Mental and emotional health and development.

    (3) Drug use and misuse, including the misuse of tobacco and alcohol.

    (4) Family health and child development, including the legal and financial aspects and responsibilities of marriage and parenthood.

    (5) Oral health, vision, and hearing.

    (6) Nutrition.

    (7) Exercise, rest, and posture.

    (8) Diseases and disorders, including sickle cell anemia and related genetic diseases and disorders.

    (9) Environmental health and safety.

    (10) Community health.

(b) To the maximum extent possible, the instruction in health is structured to provide comprehensive education in health to include all the subjects in subdivision (a).

(c) There is the maximum community participation in the teaching of health including classroom participation by practicing professional health and safety personnel in the community.

(d) Pupils gain appreciation for the importance and value of lifelong health and the need for each individual's personal responsibility for his or her own health.

Integrated Services Center Links School, Family, and Community

*by Andrea Zetlin, California State University at Los Angeles and The
National Center on Education in the Inner Cities; and Robert Bilovsky,
Principal, Murchison Street Elementary School, Los Angeles*

The Murchison Street Elementary School in Los Angeles, in partnership with the California State University at Los Angeles (CSULA), has established an innovative multiservice center to help students and their families access health and support services. The Family Services Center uses an integrated, client-centered approach to coordinate school, community, and family resources. By streamlining school and community services and by inviting parents to become more involved in the education of their children, Murchison is working to improve student learning and inner-city family life.

Located in East Los Angeles, a low-income section of the city where many families do not speak English, Murchison is among the lowest-achieving elementary schools in the Los Angeles Unified School District (LAUSD). Many families live below the poverty line, lack adequate health care, suffer from poor nutrition, and live in substandard housing located in crime- and drug-infested neighborhoods.

Through the CSULA partnership, supported by an SB 620 (Healthy Start Support Services for Children Act) operational grant, Murchison is striving to modify curriculum, introduce more effective teaching strategies, and integrate the delivery of services by linking them to resources within the community through the Family Services Center.

Creating a Hub for Coordinated Services

Murchison's Integrated Services Center is designed like a wheel, with the Family Services Center, the primary agency, at the hub. Students and families are referred to the center by teachers, school counselors, psychologists, and nurses. On-site services, such as counseling and health care, are available at this central location. Resource and referral services are also available to parents, who ordinarily must navigate alone through a patchwork of disjointed service providers and programs.

The "spokes" extending from the Family Services Center are staff members, who help connect school resources with those of the community, such as agencies providing health, mental health, social

Adapted, with permission, from an article in the September, 1992, issue of the *CEIC Review*.

welfare, and juvenile justice services. By collaborating with other agencies, the center is better able to meet the specific needs of students and their families.

Making Parents a Part of the Process

The designers of the Family Services Center believe that parental involvement in the education of their children is essential to successful service coordination. At Murchison a parent center adjacent to the Family Services Center provides this critical link between parents, the school, and numerous outside service providers.

Informal meetings between parents and teachers are promoted through weekly discussion groups called *platicas* or "parent talks," which are conducted in both English and Spanish for parents, teachers, a CSULA faculty member, and a parent coordinator. Topics, suggested by parents, have included health issues, children talking back, problems with a divorced spouse, communication in the family, self-esteem, and sexual abuse. Through these meetings and other weekly and monthly gatherings, parents help develop instructional materials for the classroom and sponsor activities, such as a monthly parent newsletter and a Family Sports Day.

A parent-to-parent mentor program trains parent mentors to assist new immigrant families and other parents who find their life situations especially stressful and complex. Mentors regularly meet with a CSULA faculty member and the Parent Center coordinator to review cases and receive guidance.

The Critical Community Link

Matching available resources to parents' most pressing needs is a primary goal of the Family Services Center. Parents ranked dental care, immunization, and vision care as the most needed health services and family counseling and drug and alcohol counseling as mental health service priorities. Job training and English as a second language (ESL) classes were the most requested adult education programs.

Since nearly 80 percent of the students who attend Murchison Street Elementary School live in Ramona Gardens, a neighborhood public housing project, Murchison teamed up with the Ramona Gardens Community Service Center, a community agency providing a variety of services to residents. Some services now jointly sponsored by Ramona Gardens and the center are housed in the Murchison Street School and include a homework and tutoring club, a mentor program that includes the "Keeper of the Dream" speakers' program, and adult education classes that include ESL, Vocational ESL, GED, and job training. A Department of Public Social Services representative from Ramona Gardens regularly attends the meetings at the Parent Center to answer parents' questions about obtaining services.

The center is also collaborating with the Los Angeles County Department of Children's Services and Public Social Services of Los Angeles. Staff from the Department of Children's Services act as case managers, working with referred families to prevent out-of-home placement. The Family Services Center has also cultivated a working relationship with La Cada, a local nonprofit agency that provides educational and treatment services for substance and alcohol abuse. La Cada provides a drug prevention program for fourth and fifth graders at Murchison and parent classes in the parent center. Murchison also works directly with social workers from the Latino Family Preservation Project and the University of Southern California Dental School, which provides preventive dental education and care to students and parents. Social work interns and counseling trainees from CSULA assist in developing comprehensive family service plans with CSULA faculty and center staff. They also provide families with short-term counseling.

With the Family Services Center as a unifying force, the Murchison Street Elementary School is successfully coordinating school and community resources. Working systematically with community organizations, agencies, health care providers, and CSULA staff, Murchison is creating an environment where students and their families may practice behaviors that promote their physical and mental health and well-being.

Project TEACH Recommendations on Preservice Teacher Training in Health Education

Project TEACH, funded by the California Department of Education and College Health 2000, was designed to improve preservice teacher training in health education. All colleges and universities providing teacher training in California were invited to participate. The project examined current practices and collaboratively developed recommendations. These recommendations, issued in 1993, are being used by participating institutions to help new teachers promote health literacy among their students more effectively. The Project TEACH recommendations, exemplary only, are presented as follows: [1]

1. Universities/colleges should offer two separate courses—one for single-subject credential candidates (secondary) and one for multiple-subject credential candidates (elementary).

2. The courses should each be three units (semester or quarter) in length, and there should be a minimum of 40 to 50 contact hours between the students and the instructor.

3. Challenges to the course (credit by examination) should not be allowed. Students should receive credit for the course only by completing the course requirements.

4. CPR certification must cover infant-child and adult CPR as well as choking emergencies (American Red Cross Community CPR or American Heart Association B-level).

5. Instructors are expected to utilize the *Health Framework* and familiarize the students with mandated areas of instruction and *Education Code* sections related to health education.

6. The courses should deal primarily with the health status and health instruction of children and adolescents. A personal health and wellness text (of the type used in introductory college personal health courses)

---

[1] For more information on Project TEACH, contact Priscilla Naworski, Director, Healthy Kids Resource Center, Alameda County Office of Education; and Director, Project TEACH.

is *not* appropriate for use in these teacher education courses.

7. The course for the multiple-subject (elementary) teachers should:

    a. Make prospective teachers aware of health issues related to children.

    b. Make prospective teachers aware of the structure of a comprehensive school health system.

    c. Help prospective teachers become familiar with the materials and methods used in comprehensive school health education.

    d. Utilize a variety of instructional strategies to model possible health education strategies.

    e. Include use of an appropriate text and/or instructional materials that will enable students to become familiar with lesson plans, resources for health education, instructional techniques, and the like.

    f. Acquaint prospective teachers with the year 2000 objectives that affect K–6 students and the health emphasis of *It's Elementary*.

8. The course for single-subject (secondary) teachers should:

    a. Acquaint prospective teachers with the year 2000 objectives for students in grades seven through twelve and the health emphasis of *Second to None*.

    b. Make prospective teachers aware of the structure of a comprehensive school health system.

    c. Teach prospective teachers how to integrate health instruction into their single-subject curriculum.

    d. Acquaint prospective teachers with the health problems and concerns of adolescents.

Included are such topics as teenage pregnancy, acne, sexually transmitted diseases, steroids, substance abuse, abusive relationships, mental health, injury prevention, and nutrition.

e. Emphasize the relationship between health and student performance.

9. Rename poorly named courses to reflect *what should be taught* in the course. Suggested course names may include:

Health Education for Elementary Teachers

Health Education for Secondary Teachers

Some course titles that would *not* be appropriate are Personal Health, Contemporary Health Issues, Health, Substance Abuse and Nutrition Education, Health and Hygiene, Nutrition, Fitness, Biology, and Health Studies.

10. Students who take a personal health course at a junior college or at another school should not be allowed to have that course fill the obligation for the health education for teachers requirement. Universities should instruct their credential analyst to require students to take the specific course in health education for teachers.

11. When universities offer only the combined course (for both multiple- and single-subject teachers), care must be taken that multiple-subject teachers are trained in content and teaching methods. Single-subject teachers must be trained in how to infuse/integrate their curriculum with health topics. This becomes a difficult task with the limited class time available. For this reason, recommendation 1 should be given top priority.

Publications Available from the Department of Education

This publication is one of over 600 that are available from the California Department of Education. Some of the more recent publications or those most widely used are the following:

Item no.	Title (Date of publication)	Price
1063	Adoption Recommendations of the Curriculum Development and Supplemental Materials Commission, 1992: California Basic Instructional Materials in Science (1992)	$5.50
0883	The Ages of Infancy: Caring for Young, Mobile, and Older Infants (videocassette and guide) (1990)*	65.00
0973	The American Indian: Yesterday, Today, and Tomorrow (1991)	6.50
1079	Beyond Retention: A Study of Retention Rates, Practices, and Successful Alternatives in California (1993)	4.25
1067	California Private School Directory, 1993-94 (1993)	16.00
1086	California Public Education: A Decade After *A Nation at Risk* (1993)	4.75
1091	California Public School Directory (1994)	16.00
1036	California Strategic Plan for Parental Involvement in Education (1992)	5.75
0488	Caught in the Middle: Educational Reform for Young Adolescents in California Public Schools (1987)	6.75
0874	The Changing History–Social Science Curriculum: A Booklet for Parents (1990)	10/5.00†
1053	The Changing History–Social Science Curriculum: A Booklet for Parents (Spanish) (1993)	10/5.00†
0867	The Changing Language Arts Curriculum: A Booklet for Parents (1990)	10/5.00†
1115	The Changing Language Arts Curriculum: A Booklet for Parents (Korean) (1993)	10/5.00†
0928	The Changing Language Arts Curriculum: A Booklet for Parents (Spanish) (1991)	10/5.00†
0777	The Changing Mathematics Curriculum: A Booklet for Parents (1989)	10/5.00†
0891	The Changing Mathematics Curriculum: A Booklet for Parents (Spanish) (1991)	10/5.00†
1072	Commodity Administrative Manual (1993)	13.00
1102	Coordinated Compliance Review Manual, 1993-94 (1993)	8.00
1101	Coordinated Compliance Review Training Guide (1993)	12.00
0978	Course Models for the History–Social Science Framework, Grade Five—United States History and Geography: Making a New Nation (1991)	8.50
1034	Course Models for the History–Social Science Framework, Grade Six—World History and Geography: Ancient Civilizations (1993)	9.50
1132	Course Models for the History–Social Science Framework, Grade Seven—World History and Geography: Medieval and Early Modern Times (1994)	12.75
1093	Differentiating the Core Curriculum and Instruction to Provide Advanced Learning Opportunities (1994)	6.50
1045	Discoveries of Infancy: Cognitive Development and Learning (videocassette and guide) (1992)*	65.00
0976	Economic Education Mandate: Handbook for Survival (1991)	7.75
1098	English as a Second Language: Implementing Effective Adult Education Programs (1993)	6.00
1046	English-as-a-Second-Language Model Standards for Adult Education Programs (1992)	7.00
0041	English–Language Arts Framework for California Public Schools (1987)	5.00
0927	English–Language Arts Model Curriculum Standards: Grades Nine Through Twelve (1991)	6.00
1056	Essential Connections: Ten Keys to Culturally Sensitive Care (videocassette and guide) (1993)*	65.00
1124	Exemplary Program Standards for Child Development Programs Serving Preschool and School-Age Children (Spanish) (1994)	5.50
0751	First Moves: Welcoming a Child to a New Caregiving Setting (videocassette and guide) (1988)*	65.00
0839	Flexible, Fearful, or Feisty: The Different Temperaments of Infants and Toddlers (videocassette and guide) (1990)*	65.00
0804	Foreign Language Framework for California Public Schools (1989)	6.50
1116	The Framework in Focus: Answers to Key Questions About the English–Language Arts Framework (1993)	5.50
0809	Getting in Tune: Creating Nurturing Relationships with Infants and Toddlers (videocassette and guide) (1990)*	65.00
1089	Greatest Hits in Environmental Education (1993)	7.00
1130	Guide and Criteria for Program Quality Review—Elementary Level (1994)	10.00
1131	Guide and Criteria for Program Quality Review—Middle Level (1994)	11.25
0986	Handbook for Teaching Korean-American Students (1992)‡	5.50
1064	Health Framework for California Public Schools, Kindergarten Through Grade Twelve (1994)	8.50
0734	Here They Come: Ready or Not—Report of the School Readiness Task Force (Full Report) (1988)	5.50
0712	History–Social Science Framework for California Public Schools (1988)	7.75
1114	Implementation of Middle Grade Reforms in California Public Schools (1993)	6.50
1071	Independent Study Operations Manual (1993)	30.00
0878	Infant/Toddler Caregiving: A Guide to Creating Partnerships with Parents (1990)	10.00
0880	Infant/Toddler Caregiving: A Guide to Language Development and Communication (1990)	10.00

*Videocassette also available in Chinese (Cantonese) and Spanish at the same price.
†The price for 100 booklets is $30; the price for 1,000 booklets is $230. A set of one of each of the parent booklets in English is $3; a set in Spanish is also $3.
‡Also available at the same price for students who speak Cantonese, Japanese, Pilipino, and Portuguese.

Item no.	Title (Date of publication)	Price
0877	Infant/Toddler Caregiving: A Guide to Routines (1990)	$10.00
0879	Infant/Toddler Caregiving: A Guide to Setting Up Environments (1990)	10.00
0876	Infant/Toddler Caregiving: A Guide to Social–Emotional Growth and Socialization (1990)	10.00
1128	Instructional Materials Approved for Legal Compliance (1994)	14.00
1024	It's Elementary! Elementary Grades Task Force Report (1992)	6.50
0869	It's Not Just Routine: Feeding, Diapering, and Napping Infants and Toddlers (videocassette and guide) (1990)*	65.00
1107	Literature for History–Social Science, Kindergarten Through Grade Eight (1993)	8.00
1066	Literature for Science and Mathematics (1993)	9.50
1033	Mathematics Framework for California Public Schools, 1992 Edition (1992)	6.75
0929	Model Curriculum Standards, Grades Nine Through Twelve (1985)	5.50
1113	On Alert! Gang Prevention: School In-service Guidelines (1994)	6.50
1065	Physical Education Framework for California Public Schools, Kindergarten Through Grade Twelve (1994)	6.75
0845	Physical Education Model Curriculum Standards, Grades Nine Through Twelve (1991)	5.50
1119	Prelude to Performance Assessment in the Arts (1994)	8.00
1032	Program Guidelines for Individuals Who Are Severely Orthopedically Impaired (1992)	8.00
1094	Program Quality Review Training Materials for Elementary and Middle Level Schools (1994)	7.50
0979	Readings for the Christopher Columbus Quincentenary (1992)	2.75†
1048	Read to Me: Recommended Readings for Children Ages Two Through Seven (1992)	5.50
0831	Recommended Literature, Grades Nine Through Twelve (1990)	5.50
0895	Recommended Readings in Spanish Literature: Kindergarten Through Grade Eight (1991)	4.25
1112	Resource Guide: Conferences, Workshops, and Training Opportunities for District and County Business Office Staff (1993)	5.50
0753	Respectfully Yours: Magda Gerber's Approach to Professional Infant/Toddler Care (videocassette and guide) (1988)*	65.00
1118	Roads to the Future: Final Report (1994)	10.00
1117	Roads to the Future: Summary Report (1994)	8.00
1088	School District Organization Handbook (1993)	16.00
1042	School Nutrition Facility Planning Guide (1992)	8.00
1038	Science Facilities Design in California Public Schools (1992)	6.25
0870	Science Framework for California Public Schools (1990)	8.00
1087	Secondary Textbook Review: Mathematical Analysis, Grades 9–12 (1993)	11.50
1040	Second to None: A Vision of the New California High School (1992)	5.75
0970	Self-assessment Guide for School District Fiscal Policy Teams: Facilities Planning and Construction (1991)	4.50
0980	Simplified Buying Guide: Child and Adult Care Food Program (1992)	8.50
0752	Space to Grow: Creating a Child Care Environment for Infants and Toddlers (videocassette and guide) (1988)*	65.00
1043	Success for Beginning Teachers: The California New Teacher Project, 1988–1992 (1992)	5.50
1134	Teachers' Catalog of Grants, Fellowships, and Awards (1994)	5.50
1044	Together in Care: Meeting the Intimacy Needs of Infants and Toddlers in Groups (videocassette and guide) (1992)*	65.00
0846	Toward a State of Esteem: The Final Report of the California Task Force to Promote Self-esteem and Personal and Social Responsibility (1990)	5.00
0758	Visions for Infant/Toddler Care: Guidelines for Professional Caregiving (1989)	6.50
0805	Visual and Performing Arts Framework for California Public Schools (1989)	7.25
1016	With History–Social Science for All: Access for Every Student (1992)	5.50
0989	Work Permit Handbook (1991)	7.75
1073	Writing Assessment Handbook: High School (1993)	9.25

*Videocassette also available in Chinese (Cantonese) and Spanish at the same price.
†Also available in quantities of 10 for $7.50 (item number 9875); 30 for $20 (9876); and 100 for $60 (9877).

Orders should be directed to:

California Department of Education
Bureau of Publications, Sales Unit
P.O. Box 271
Sacramento, CA 95812-0271

Please include the item number for each title ordered.

Mail orders must be accompanied by a check, a purchase order, or a credit card number, including expiration date (VISA or MasterCard only). Purchase orders without checks are accepted from governmental agencies only. Telephone orders will be accepted toll-free (1-800-995-4099) for credit card purchases only. Sales tax should be added to all orders from California purchasers. Stated prices, which include shipping charges to anywhere in the United States, are subject to change.

Publications Catalog: Educational Resources and its supplement contain illustrated, annotated listings of departmental publications. Free copies may be obtained by writing to the address given above or by calling (916) 445-1260.

R94-06 (Second printing) 003-0006-94 300 8-94 20M